investigating

POLYGONS and POLYHEDRA

with

Allen W. Banbury   Sheldon G. Berman   Harry Erickson

A Teacher's Resource Book of Ideas for Grades K-6

20020

ARLINGTON-HEWS, INC.

VANCOUVER / PHILADELPHIA

Allen W. Banbury is an Elementary Mathematics Specialist with the School District of Philadelphia. He has a B.A. in Mathematics from the University of Hawaii and a M.S. in Mathematics Education from the University of Pennsylvania. He has been teaching mathematics for 27 years to students from kindergarten to adulthood.

Acknowledgement: We are indebted to all the primary and elementary children, including our own Michelle, Lorraine and Zachary, who have kept our eyes open to the wonders of our world as we learned together.

Sheldon G. Berman has his B.A. in mathematics from Temple University and a Master's degree in Alternative Education from Indiana University. He has been teaching on the secondary level in the School District of Philadelphia for 20 years.

Production Editor   W.M. Swystun

SECOND EDITION

Printed in Canada

Canadian Cataloguing in Publication Data
Banbury, Allen W.
   Investigating polygons and polyhedra with Googolplex® :
a teacher's resource book of ideas for
grades K-6

   Bibliography: p.
   ISBN 0-921208-00-6

   1. Geometry – Study and teaching (Elementary)
2. Polygons. 3. Polyhedra – Models. I.
Berman, Sheldon G.   II. Erickson, Harry.
III. Title.
QA462.B35 1988   372.7   C88-091071-2

Library Of Congress Cataloguing-in-Publication Data
Banbury, Allen W.
   Investigating polygons and polyhedra with Googolplex®

   Bibliography: p.

   1. Polygons – Study and teaching (Primary)
2. Polyhedra – Study and teaching (Primary)
3. Polygons — Study and teaching (Elementary)
4. Polyhedra — Study and teaching (Elementary)
I. Berman, Sheldon G.   II. Erickson, Harry.
III. Title: IV. Title: Googolplex.
QA491.B25 1988   516'.15   88-946
ISBN 0-921208-00-6 (pbk.)

Contents

Cover photo: Open pattern with pentagons and decagonal domes.

Preface

This manual has been written as a resource book for all teachers or those who intend to teach; to help them gain a better understanding of some of the more intriguing aspects of the geometry that is taught in the elementary grades, and to help them to learn and use a method of presenting that content. The activities described here are designed around a set of geometric building materials called Googolplex.

The fact that this material and this manual have been chosen, indicates that the reader is probably convinced of the importance of helping children to develop geometric and spatial understandings. We are convinced of the importance of these understandings in the other areas of the curriculum such as social studies, science, art and even reading, where it is very helpful to have the ability to visualize the setting of a story as described by the author.

The authors of this manual believe that almost all learning of geometry at the elementary level involves hands-on contact with that content in some material way. This hands-on contact must be accompanied by the opportunity to respond to that contact, both at the time of the experience and afterwards, as the students think about what was observed and what it might mean. The activities outlined here assume that the student has hands-on contact with the Googolplex material and is not just observing demonstrations. The underlying principal is;

I hear and I forget;
I see and I remember;
I do and I understand.

This manual is divided into three sections. The first section is an **Introduction** to the materials known as Googolplex. The second section, **Notes to the Teacher,** provides general guidance on teaching and learning geometry and on the structure and use of this resource book. The **Investigations** section begins with a **Familiarization** with the materials, followed by some aspects of the geometry of flat surfaces or plane geometry through a consideration of **Polygons.** It concludes by dealing with several aspects of the geometry of solid figures by investigating **Polyhedra.**

Googolplex consists of a set of geometric building components including connectors. In its design and production, great attention has been given to the inter-relationship of pieces, and to fit and finish. The power of Googolplex lies in its ability to be used to replicate shapes and surfaces from the intriguing and marvelously inter-related world of geometry, and thus, to provide a study of the spaces in which we exist. We feel certain that the time you and your students spend with this manipulative in both free and guided exploration, will begin to develop the ability to perceive spatial relationships and will supply numerous experiences that will motivate and simplify a more formal study of geometry.

For us, investigating geometry with Googolplex has been a source of constant intellectual challenge and esthetic delight. We have tried to share that enthusiasm with you in a way that will help you to convey it to your students as you guide them through the activities in this book.

We suggest that you invest some time to get to know about both the concept and device known as Googolplex.

Please see this book and these activities as a beginning. There are a great number of ways to explore our geometrical world, and only a small number can be suggested here. We hope that you will take yourself and your students far beyond the confines of these pages.

INTRODUCTION

GOOGOLPLEX
A Very Large Number

The name Googolplex was selected for this toy because of the astonishingly complex and seemingly countless ways that the pieces can be combined to make both flat and three dimensional shapes. "Googol" is a legitimate word in the lexicon of mathematics and was first proposed by the nine-year-old nephew of Dr. Edward Kasner who was seeking a term for the extremely large number 10^{100} or ten times itself one hundred times. A googol would be written as a 1 followed by 100 zeros.[1]

10,000,000,000,000,000,000,000,000,000,000,000,000,000,000,000,000,000,000,000,000,000,000,000,000,000,000,000,000,000,000,000,000,000

By a very comfortable margin, this number exceeds the number of seconds since the Big Bang at the proposed beginning of the universe about fifteen billion years ago, give or take a few billion. That number only requires 17 zeros. If we made some rather generous assumptions, the number of cubic centimeters in that ever expanding universe today, would only be in the neighborhood of 12 with 84 zeros after it. Imagining a number of this size is practically impossible.

The existence of a number like a googol begs for a more complex sequel. As a result, googol was then applied as an exponent to ten, that is, 10^{googol} which would be a 1 followed by a googol of zeros. The recognized name "googolplex" was given to that number and even if a million zeros were placed in every one of the cubic centimeters in the universe, we would be woefully short of the number of zeros needed to write it. It would take about three billion (3,000,000,000) universes like ours, similarly filled with zeros to finally get the required number of zeros. A number of this size, while not infinite, is still large enough to leave us either gasping or numb, and remember, all those zeros are just for writing the number down.

And if a googolplex is challenging, what about googolplex + 1? What about $10^{googolplex}$ or googolplex ^{googolplex}? Can a finite number be awesomely unreasonable?

1. Kasner, E., & J. Newman, 1940, Mathematics and the Imagination. p. 23. New York: Simon & Schuster.

A Construction Toy And Much More

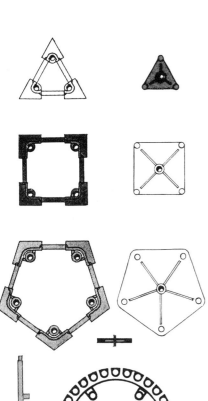

The design of **Googolplex** components is beautifully simple: the three most basic regular polygons, the triangle, square and pentagon, are presented as

FRAMES

designed so that each **edge** is the same length. Each frame has a matching

FACE PLATE

that can be easily attached to sockets just inside each **vertex** of the frame. Each face plate has a socket in its **center** (also known as its centroid, or balance point). The frames are readily attached to each other at their hinges by clever hinge-like

CONNECTORS

that allow the **dihedral angle** between the frames to be adjusted through a complete rotation from a zero angle with the frames touching to a full rotation with the frames now touching on their opposite faces. Each of the connectors has a socket at its **midpoint.** The sockets near the vertices of the frames, in the center of each face plate, and at the midpoint of each connector will accept the ends of

RODS

that have extensions at their midpoints to allow for other attachments and to assist in inserting and removing the rods with small fingers. In addition to these components, there are

WHEELS

which attach to the pentagonal face plates and which have 30 sockets on each side spaced around their circumference that will also accept the rods. The centers of the face plates can be connected with

AXLES

which will allow any structures that are attached to the face plates, including the wheels, to rotate freely. As a building toy, Googolplex is infinitely versatile and satisfying. As a purposeful educational device, it is a powerful way to recreate many of the two and three dimensional structures that are found everywhere in the natural environment.

The basic Googolplex® components

Notes to the Teacher
Attitudes for Teaching and Learning

As educators, we utilize techniques that come from a variety of sources, most especially from our own experiences as students. For many of us, the geometry curriculum was sparse in the elementary grades, possibly limited to the rote memorization of vocabulary and shape identification. Further, that study was not tied into our real world of experience. As essential as geometry and spatial visualization are to the preparation for higher mathematics courses and the understanding of our physical world, it is not surprising that so many students have faced high school geometry with great anxiety and have taken no courses beyond geometry unless they were required to do so. Very few elementary teachers have had any mathematics beyond geometry or second year algebra. And yet, with this sparse background, they are expected to work with all the elementary grades and teach the marvelous and exciting content of elementary geometry and help students develop a spatial sense so that their world will be more accessible.

It is our hope that your involvement with these materials shows a personal commitment to growth. We hope that your students will receive the same enthusiastic, knowledgeable and skilled instruction that you received as a student from your most memorable teachers no matter what the subject matter was. We further hope that your students will leave your classroom with a heightened sense of curiosity about things that are essentially geometric, and a more highly refined set of skills for analyzing, visualizing, and describing the spatial situations and relationships within which they are immersed.

To this end, we offer these methods and activities for you and your students.

Teaching and Learning Geometry

Children enter our classrooms with a whole range of skills and conceptual frameworks with respect to geometry. In many cases, the spatial sense of early elementary children is more highly developed than the numerical sense. Building on this strength can be very helpful in developing other mathematical understandings and in developing a lifetime "I can do it" attitude towards mathematics.

These understandings are not often categorized in the child's mind as "geometry," and indeed, our students are often surprised to find that the label applies to anything other than a seemingly sterile study of figures on paper or a chalkboard. Those figures on paper, which are adequate for showing flat figures, are woefully inadequate for portraying three dimensional objects that do not fit well on flat text book pages, or on any chalkboard. Children playing on a jungle-gym or building with a set of blocks or construction toys gain more understanding about spatial relations than they may ever gain as a result of their formal education. As teachers, we must engage the children in a dialogue with the material in their natural world through experimentation, and in a dialogue with their learning peers (including the teacher) through spoken and written language, pictorial representation and demonstration. In this way, the learners will begin to explore the boundaries of their knowledge in a reflective way and push those boundaries out into a new territory.

If you were to lay out a map of the geometry curriculum, and plot the movement of a child through that curriculum, you would find they have usually followed a zig-zag path. Children rarely learn content in the same sequence that academicians invent to organize that content. In their investigations, the children's activities are very liable to move beyond the teacher's level of understanding and the teacher will run out of "right answers." To many, including the students, this process is enlivening as the students take the teacher and the rest of the class onto new ground. Specific situations are worked through; generalities emerge and are tested; vocabulary is located or invented as necessary; extensions are proposed and explored. In this fashion, children grow in their knowledge of geometry and in their skill for approaching new situations in a rational way.

Believing that this is a powerful way for children to learn, what are some of the actions that teachers can take so that student's responses produce understanding? Teachers must be, or must work on becoming, models for inquiry. We need to self-consciously let our students see us in the many phases of inquiry and let them "listen in" as we go through the process. Some of the most talented teachers can be distinguished by the types of questions they ask in motivating the students' movement through the course content, and the way that they keep the students involved in the seemingly fresh and original discovery and generation of that content. They become intelligent fellow travelers, not just guides who dispense truth and eliminate all problems before the class is aware that a problem is coming. Children need to see teachers **messing about** and exploring new situations whether they are real or simulated. They need to see us **mulling over** what has been found out, and in the process, they will watch us **modeling** an approach for dealing with new situations or content. As a mnemonic device, we offer the 3 M's of teaching, namely **Messing about, Mulling over** and **Modeling.** With so much rightful attention being paid to "problem solving," or "critical thinking," as essential skills for all people at all times, the 3 M's are a powerful way to help develop reasoning abilities in our students.

All of this calls on your skills as teacher and actor. You must skillfully feign ignorance when you know what is going on, both to motivate the study of the content, and to engage the class in assisting classmates who have yet to understand the material. Your questions can't be transparent though, or you will be found out. With your assistance, **THEY must be allowed to discover the questions and answers.** You must act as though a student's discovery is brand new when it is well known. You must forget that an algorithm or rule exists for a situation until the students invent their own and then you help them verify it. You must be an opportunist who finds the content in the seemingly random work of the students. You must become an intellectual peer who engages in a dialogue with the learners, asks for clarification, and poses possible courses of action. YOU must be a participant.

Useful Tools and Techniques

Some among us are blessed with strong hands and tough fingernails. For the rest, ingenuity and the intelligent application of some simple tools will help in **assembling** and **disassembling** the Googolplex pieces.

Assembling pieces by attaching connectors or face plates is made easier by placing the frame on a flat hard surface like a table, and pressing the face plate or connector into place.

Disassembling your creations is made easier by holding a frame in each hand and twisting the frames so that they detach themselves from the connector that holds them. Connectors may be removed from frames in this fashion also. Removing frames and plates from finished shapes is often helped by pushing from the other side with eraser end of an **unsharpened** pencil. Removing plates that are tightly attached to frames is much easier if you insert the point or vertex of a triangular frame between the frame and face plate and pry or twist it loose. Prying from several points is helpful. The removal of a particularly difficult connector from a frame can be accomplished by placing the frame and the connector on top of a triangle plate on a table so that the connector rests on the bumps of the plate, and then pressing the frame out from underneath the connector. Rods can be removed by wiggling them around a small amount so that they work themselves loose.

USEFUL TOOLS:

Measuring instruments can be introduced as they are deemed appropriate by local curriculum or student maturity. We recommend having a retractable metal **tape measure,** with both a standard and a metric scale, preferably one that can be carried with the teacher at all times, either clipped to the belt or in a pocket. Student **rulers** with appropriate metric and standard scales should be available. Clear plastic **protractors** can be used for the measurement of angles on a surface (plane angles) and with a procedure described in "Polyhedra 2," they can be used to estimate the size of the angle between two planes (dihedral angle). The possession of these tools by the teacher will allow measurement to occur in spontaneous situations as they arise, with the student witnessing the appropriate use of a measuring instrument in the context of real inquiry.

Mirrors can be an extremely powerful tool for introducing, demonstrating and developing the idea of symmetry. One of the best choices for mirrors is the type of rectangular metal mirror that is sold by sporting goods stores to be used while camping. These are about 9 cm x 12 cm and often have two reflective surfaces protected with a thin plastic laminating film. Peeling and using one leaves the other protected until scratches degrade the exposed surface and make replacement desirable. Two such mirrors hinged together at a long edge with tape on the back, allow for producing symmetric images with many axes and planes of symmetry.

Overhead projectors are highly effective for placing images from this book in front of your class. Making transparencies and thermal blackline masters on a photocopier will eliminate the need to separate the pages from this book.

Storage containers are provided with each set. The boxed set is held in a plastic tray that gives young hands a chance to classify and sort materials. A first step for the user would be the reinforcement of all the corners of the box with transparent tape to prolong its life. The lamination of the enclosed poster would also be time well spent. When alternative packaging is needed resealable heavy duty 2.5 + mil (thousandths of an inch thick) plastic freezer bags in the one gallon size are quite serviceable. Each bag with half of an Advanced 900 set would then have enough pieces for a working group of three or four students.

Organizing for Instruction

GROUP SIZE

This type of learning style requires that children have access to enough materials so that they go through the activities suggested by the teacher. These actions are more powerful as the students explain, describe, compare, predict and write about what is happening. The amount of this exchange is enhanced if students work in groups. We expect that any answer from a group will reflect the beliefs of the entire group. We expect that within reason, any member of the group should be able to explain the group's response. We strongly suggest that those groups be no larger than four students.

WORKING SPACE

This type of material requires a flat and fairly large working area. The primary grades often work on a rug on the floor. If this is the case, they will need a hard surface to build on like a drawing board as described in **Useful Tools and Techniques, Assembling and Disassembling.** In classes of older children, work tables need to be provided or assembled from student desks. Keeping the desks tightly grouped together will help prevent some of the dropping of pieces that annoys both students and teachers.

MATERIALS MANAGEMENT

The storage of the materials in the original box or in plastic bags as described in **Useful Tools and Techniques, Storage Containers** will make your job much easier. A designated "stock clerk" or other titled person should be responsible for collecting and distributing a group's materials. You may wish to have a formal inventory process with the students counting out and counting back. This seems excessive though unless you are seeking counting activities for the kindergarten and first grade students.

The Investigations

This source book has been written as a series of investigations. The investigations are written as dialogues with suitable information provided to guide the teacher. This information appears in the heading of the unit, in the TEACHER ACTION column and in the STUDENT RESPONSE column.

The heading of each unit contains the following specific information to help you get organized for instruction:

GRADES gives our estimate of the children that could profitably engage in all or parts of the activity. Here, your professional discretion is essential in selecting and structuring the content. All activities are not appropriate for all grades.

GOALS lists the anticipated learnings in the unit.

MATERIALS needed for the lesson in addition to Googolplex and student supplied items like pencils and lined paper, will be listed here, for example, rulers, graph paper, matrix sheets, overhead transparencies and projector, etc.

After each heading, the dialogues have been divided into TEACHER ACTION on the left side of the page, and probable STUDENT RESPONSE on the right side. In anticipation of the growth of skill on the part of the teacher, the notations on both sides of the dialogue will be less specific as you get further into the material.

Notations on the TEACHER ACTION side of the page will be of several sorts:

Suggested phrasing of statements are in **bold face type.**

These statements will be questions for the students, directions to the students, or information. Alternative language for more mature students will be placed in [braces]. Where specific vocabulary is used, the words will be **bold.**

Ordinary type face entries will list the many other activities of the teacher such as showing materials, and illustrations to the students with a sketch when appropriate. The illustrations will range from a sketch on the board to a page in this book. An overhead projector and a transparency will prove extremely helpful here.

There are other entries to assist you:

TIPS provide information of many sorts for the teacher on underlying strategy and interrelations.

ASIDES consist of information that is not focused on the Goals, but which can be shared with the students when appropriate.

EXTENSIONS will be indicated where a related learning activity seems like fertile ground for student growth or for independent exploration.

ANNOTATIONS of your own should be written in as you gain experience and begin to develop and trust your own insights.

The STUDENT RESPONSE column will contain several types of information:

Illustrations of the types of constructions the students might make will be shown.

Examples will be given of statements the students might make.

Possibilities for a written response to the situation will be specified.

Clarifying responses that you might make will be indicated.

TIPS will be found in the STUDENT RESPONSE section also.

The Lesson

GETTING READY

As with any instruction, the most important process is getting ready. **The most effective preparation consists of actually playing with the material yourself.** This can be done by the reveal method where you slide two pieces of paper down the page to expose first the TEACHER ACTION and after following through with the students moves, the appropriate STUDENT RESPONSE. **Because of the wide age range of the target population of these materials and the variations of local curricula, it is essential that the teacher go through the units, select the activities, and alter the vocabulary and phrasing as necessary because of the maturity of their students.** The ordinary tasks of preparation such as locating and gathering materials, duplicating pages, and making transparencies are ongoing jobs that must also be attended to.

FREE PLAY

In recognition of the value of play as a time when many unexpected learnings can be introduced and arrived at naturally, we strongly recommend that the first part of each lesson (perhaps ten minutes) be devoted to **Free Play** with the materials. As this is taking place, you have a natural opportunity to move around the working groups, look at content in a spontaneous way and make appropriate remarks. You can review the content of previous lessons as that content is revealed in the work of the youngsters. Perhaps you will find prime examples of structures and ideas that will be generated in the days lesson. As you become more familiar with the content, you will see the beginnings of investigations that are to come. A mirror in your hand allows for symmetry experiences and a tape measure on your belt allows for comparisons of length, height and perimeter. **Free Play** time is an opportunity to insert some vocabulary, ask seminal questions, identify weaknesses, and receive informal feedback from the youngsters.

THE LESSON

At the end of **Free Play,** which has provided the essential warmup for the lesson, and with the work of a student as a possible transition, set off on the lesson. The structure and content of the teacher/student exchange can follow the plan of the "investigations." The other aspects of the lesson will be the same as for any other lesson you conduct and should include at least the components of reviewing past learnings as they are relevant, stating the goals of the lesson, and summarizing the content.

INVESTIGATIONS

Familiarization 1
A First Exposure

GRADES: **Kindergarten to Sixth**

GOALS: To become familiar with the names and properties of the individual pieces.
To relate the shapes to objects in their world.

MATERIALS: Paper and materials for drawing the shapes, matrix sheets. (Blackline master found on page 52.)

TEACHER ACTION	STUDENT RESPONSE

During **Free Play,** as you are discussing the children's structures with them, stress proper terminology.

Bring **Free Play** to a close

What can you tell me about the pieces your team has?

Write their responses on the board.

What names would you use for the pieces you have? Do all the members in your team agree on the name?

Write the names offered by the students next to sketches of the pieces on the board.

Call the **pentagon** a "five sided figure," "a five angled figure," and "a pentagon," interchangeably at the start if the children don't know the proper name, and move to the exclusive use of the terms "pentagon" and "pentagonal" over time. It may take some effort and strategy, like that above, to move **frame, plate** and **axle** into their vocabulary.

Look for descriptive information appropriate to their age.

From primary students you might expect phrases like "blue sticks, red squares, etc." With the older children probe for more specific descriptions like "a red plastic square with a hole in the middle and a cross on one side."

All classes will have several who will know **square, triangle, rod,** and **wheel.** When they see the role of the **connector,** its label becomes apparent.

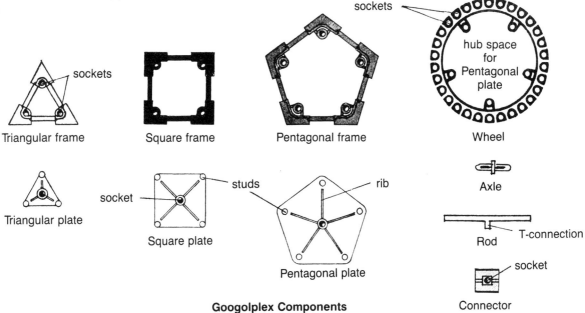

Googolplex Components

Pick one of the pieces. How would you describe it to me on the telephone so that I would have a good picture in my mind?

Draw a representation of the shape on the board as it is described in words. Don't watch them. Make them communicate their meaning with words.

Let them see the effect of inexact language. Look for words and phrases with imprecise meaning and purposely interpret them incorrectly.

TIP: Being able to see your efforts will give them immediate feedback as to how their words are affecting the outcome. A variation would be to move the speaker or team so that they can't see the emerging drawing.

EXTENSION: As a team, have them write up an exact description of the piece so that the description could be used by a manufacturing plant to make the piece. Drawings could be used to assist the description. This would be an extensive project depending on the skill level of the students. Those with more skill, able to work with greater precision, would find it a more difficult task.

Can you see any of these shapes (triangle, square, pentagon) in the room? Have you seen any of these shapes outside of school?

They will find triangles in the room but few will be like these (**equilateral** and **regular**). Explore the difference between them. Squares are also scarce (floor tile, window panes, computer diskettes) but rectangles are numerous. Pentagons are in the stars on flags, in Washington (Department of Defense Building) and on the hood of Chrysler cars.

I know many who read with their lips and count on their fingers. I want to know if you can see with your hands. For each of you, find a square plate, a triangular plate and a pentagonal plate. Put them in one hand and put that hand behind you. Now, without peeking back, see if you can bring out a square plate and show it to me. Can you find a plate that has five sides? Show me a piece with a hole in the middle?

Have them place different selections behind their back and select the specified one. Have them find a blue one, [one with a right (acute, obtuse) angle]

TIP: This is also a good exercise for working with coins, colored rods and cutouts of the letters of the alphabet.

On matrix paper fill in CHARACTERISTIC on the top, SHAPE at the side. Make appropriate entries for each piece for the characteristics you choose.

Have Primary students create a picture using the shapes as the basic forms in the picture.

CHARACTERISTIC

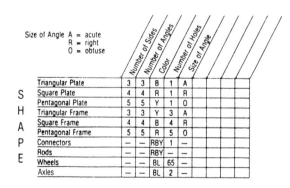

Size of Angle A = acute
R = right
O = obtuse

	Shape	Number of Sides	Number of Angles	Color	Number of Holes	Size of Angle			
S	Triangular Plate	3	3	B	1	A			
	Square Plate	4	4	R	1	R			
	Pentagonal Plate	5	5	Y	1	O			
H	Triangular Frame	3	3	Y	3	A			
A	Square Frame	4	4	B	4	R			
P	Pentagonal Frame	5	5	R	5	O			
	Connectors	—	—	RBY	1	—			
E	Rods	—	—	RBY	—	—			
	Wheels	—	—	BL	65	—			
	Axles	—	—	BL	2	—			

Table 1

Familiarization 2

GRADES: **Kindergarten to Sixth**

GOALS: To develop initial concepts of combining simple shapes to make other similar or more complex shapes. To develop observation skills and see some other aspects of the materials.

MATERIALS: Matrix sheets for recording information (blackline master found on page 52), overhead transparency of the matrix sheet and projector.

TEACHER ACTION	STUDENT RESPONSE

During **Free Play,** watch for and encourage the building of flat patterns of pieces. They may make flat shapes looking like horses, houses, cars, etc. Ask them for the name of the shape. If grade appropriate, write the name on the board or on a 3″ x 5″ card and give it to the youngster. You will find the imagination of the children limitless. They will probably not confine themselves to the **plane** but will build up off the table. Look for those characteristics of **Free Play** that are listed in **Notes to the Teacher.**

Bring **Free Play** to a close

Emphasize the need for teamwork in the lesson.

Hold up a single **square frame.**

What is this?

square, square frame

Using the square frames and the connectors, can you make a larger square?

Look for a 2 x 2 or 3 x 3 square shape.

This discussion looks at the 2 x 2. You may want to extend to the 3 x 3 or larger squares.

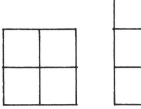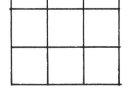

How would you describe the new square you made?

Encourage specific descriptions like those generated in the last lesson.

For example: "Four squares are connected in a larger square that is two squares tall and two squares wide"

How many squares did it take to make the larger square?

Four

An important fact about squares is that they can be used to make more squares. Can the triangle or the pentagon be used to make more triangles or pentagons? What is your guess? Can you verify your guess?

Record their team estimates on the board.

The triangles will, the pentagons will not.

As they start working, check out their work.

The work will look somewhat like this.

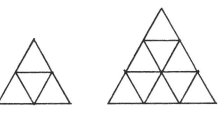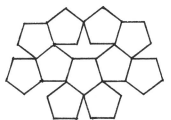

How many triangles did it take to make a larger triangle? How did that compare with the squares?

Four, or nine for the next larger size.

Do you think that any other shapes can reproduce like the square and the triangle? Can you find any that do? Will it also take four of them to make the next larger size?

They may find a suitable shape. If they make no progress, show them a 1 x 2 rectangle and have them demonstrate that it will work.

 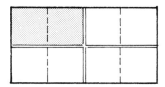 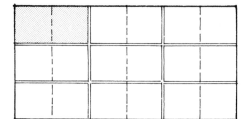

ASIDE: A more complete discussion of this is found later on in this book in the Polygon section.

EXTENSION: Have students examine the number series formed by the number of frames needed to make the sequence of larger squares, and the number of triangles necessary for the sequence of larger triangles. They will generate a series of square numbers (1, 4, 9, 16, 25, etc.) but don't tell them so, let them discover that.

Are there any pieces that will attach to themselves?

Some students will have already found that the plates will do so.

 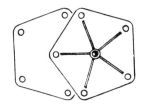

TIP: Check to see that the students position the plates with vertex studs and center sockets plugged into each other.

TIP: The result will be a little more stable if the plates face each other with "ribbed sides" or with "smooth sides"

Each team member work with only a single type of plate and see what patterns you can make.

You will find numerous **symmetric** and **asymmetric** arrays.

Move among the teams and share representative arrays made by the students.

Look for regular arrangements that follow the same pattern from plate to plate to plate.

For the rest of today, let us try some new rules. Each plate that is added must follow the pattern of the plates before it.

Move around the room and look for linear or rotational patterns.

Does anyone have any patterns that seem to get longer and longer in a straight line?

Which plate is that? Do any other plates do this?

The square plate does.

(while holding up examples) **Some of the "plate only" constructions look like modern multilevel parking garages in a big city. Some look like spiral staircases inside a lighthouse.**

 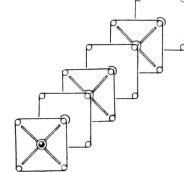

Are there both right handed and left handed staircases? (They curve up to the right or up to the left.)

Can any plate make both types of spiral staircases?

EXTENSION: Can any plate make two types of right handed staircases?

The pentagon will, depending on how sharp a turn you regularly make before you place the next plate. Putting the plates in place on the "sharp turn" staircase is quite difficult.

Look at your spiral patterns. Did you get any of them to go all the way around so that they came out above themselves?

How Many plates did it take until just before you were above the starting plate?

How is that number related to the number of sides on the plate?

Distribute matrix sheets to each student.

**In your groups, I want you to decide what should be entered in the boxes on these sheets.
Down the left side of your sheet I want you to write:**

Write on your transparency:

S
H   Triangle Plate
A   Square Plate
P   Pentagon Plate
E

Head your table with this label.

TIP: Choose the label for the table that is appropriate for your class.

CHARACTERISTIC or
PROPERTY or
ATTRIBUTE

And in the boxes across the top, write the characteristics (properties, attributes) we have found for the plates, like:

(while writing on the board)

Can be Connected
Can Make a Spiral

As a team, fill in the matrix and hand it in at the end of the period.

Move around the room to deal with any problems they are having.

Look for examples and share with the class.

All can, right and left handed.

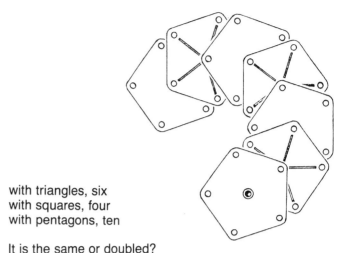

with triangles, six
with squares, four
with pentagons, ten

It is the same or doubled?

Their table will look about like this

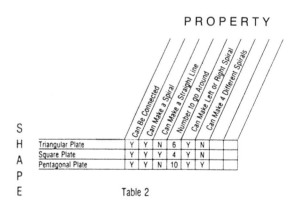

Table 2

Elicit these from the students:
Can Make a Straight Line
Number to go Around
Can make Left or Right Spiral
Can Make 4 Different Spirals

PROPERTY

	Can Be Connected	Can Make a Spiral	Can Make a Straight Line	Number to go Around	Can Make Left or Right Spiral	Can Make 4 Different Spirals	
Triangular Plate	Y	Y	N	6	Y	N	
Square Plate	Y	Y	Y	4	Y	N	
Pentagonal Plate	Y	Y	N	10	Y	Y	

Familiarization 3

GRADES: **Kindergarten to Sixth**

GOALS: To identify qualitative and quantitative relationships between the pieces.
To classify pieces by attributes.

MATERIALS: Matrix sheets, appropriate measuring instruments (rulers, protractors, pan balances), overhead transparency of matrix sheet and projector.

TEACHER ACTION	STUDENT RESPONSE

During **Free Play,** look for any signs of sorting of the pieces. Encourage this activity and try to enlist the others in the team to work on it. As appropriate, discuss the relative size of the structures or pieces, for example, the "taller" or "tallest," the "longer" or the "longest." Use your tape measure to measure the height and other dimensions of the shapes and structures. Don't expect the students to respond to these dimensions yet. This will come in later lessons.

Bring **Free Play** to a close

I would like each team to make a pile and in that pile put one of every type of piece.

Some teams will select on the basis of shape, some on the basis of shape and color.

How many different pieces does your team have in its pile?

In general, some teams will find ten types of pieces (six frames and plates, axles, connectors, rods and wheels). Some will find fourteen (those above and two additional colored connectors and two additional colored rods).

Record the responses on the board.

Why are there different answers? Where are the other four pieces coming from?

Work with them to get agreement on what makes the pieces different. If counting is going to make any sense, an agreement must be reached.

They will probably agree on language such as "there are ten different shapes" and "there are fourteen different kinds of pieces."

TIP: In preparation for this lesson, think of the attributes your students might identify and how they might measure them if appropriate.

Which of the shapes is the smallest? (purposely vague).

Expect various answers probably based on shortest length, shortest perimeter, or smallest area. Size of smallest angle and thinness might also be offered as criteria. Record their answers.

Why are there several "smallest" pieces? What does smallest mean?

Help them to explore what is being compared and why the answers differ.

The activity now becomes one of measuring and/or comparing pieces with respect to several criteria, recording that information in a coordinated way on matrix sheets and ranking the pieces in terms of these criteria. Non-numerical comparison is appropriate for the younger children.

They might compare size in side by side comparison. Angles could be compared by placing pieces on top of each other. Weight could be handled in a simple but sensitive pan balance.

With older children, go through the processes with them of deciding what to measure, how to measure it, how to record it and how to compare the results.

Children often get in line in alphabetical order, and that might also be a way to rank the pieces. This is not geometric but it is well defined.

Draw the matrix table on the board (or use the transparency of the matrix sheet and an overhead projector) and go through the process with them. Write the names of the shapes in the spaces at the left and the property in the spaces at the top. Put a "B" in the box if the indicated shape is the biggest in that characteristic and an "S" if it is the smallest.

[Or put a 1 in the box if it is the smallest and count up as they increase in size.]

Have them finish the activity. Check to see that they separate the pieces appropriately.

I want you to separate all of your pieces into four families. They will be called "the blue family," "the red family," "the yellow family" and the "black family."

Now, I want one member of the team to put your pieces into different families. Be sure that each piece has a family to belong to, and see if your teammates can guess the names of your families.

Switch roles now and try to be very clear in your family names so that you avoid confusing families.

Name a family that has no family members here?

Name a family that all the pieces belong to?

Everyone get single pieces that belong in this family, "The family of frames and plates."

Now, show me a family of pieces in that family that has all their angles equal.

Show me a smaller family in that large family of pieces whose members have more than three sides.

Show me a smaller family in this new family whose pieces have less than five sides.

Show me a smaller family whose members look like picture frames.

As a team, write a description of three families where the smallest family is in the second and the second family is in the largest.

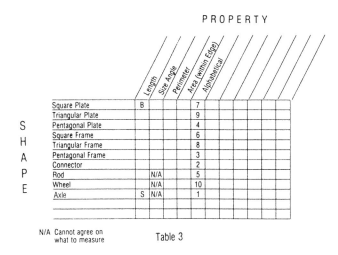

SHAPE	Length	Size Angle	Perimeter	Area (within Edge)	Alphabetical					
Square Plate	B			7						
Triangular Plate				9						
Pentagonal Plate				4						
Square Frame				6						
Triangular Frame				8						
Pentagonal Frame				3						
Connector				2						
Rod		N/A		5						
Wheel		N/A		10						
Axle	S	N/A		1						

N/A Cannot agree on what to measure   Table 3

Move from team to team to listen to the discussion and ask clarifying questions only if they aren't coming from the teammates. Probe with questions like, "What do they have in common? What do they have that none of the others have?" Often a piece will belong to more than one family. Help them to avoid this conflict.

Possible criteria for family naming might be the color (blue, red, yellow); function (frame, plate, other); shape (more than four sides, four sides or less, can't tell how many sides); number of holes (more than one hole, less than two holes), etc.

Check their oral responses. The green family, the tea cup family.

The Googolplex family, the plastic family, the building toy family, etc.

All frames and plates.

There should be no change. Some families have several names.

Pentagons and squares, frames and plates.

Square frames and plates.

Square frames.

Possibilities:

The square family in the blue family in the Googolplex family, or the plate family in the triangle family in the polygon family.

Polygons
Vocabulary and Concepts

Point:

Point in geometry is one of several undefined terms due to its essential nature. If all words are defined in relation to other words, some word will ultimately depend on itself for meaning. Mathematicians and many others avoid circular definitions.

A small dot is a "point" to most adults and children who deal with the concept. In reality, the dot only exists to indicate a position on a floor, on a map or on paper. **Points only have position.** If we make the dots larger or smaller, it is just for visual convenience. We all understand where the point is at the North Pole. We can't get there conveniently but we know where it is.

Line:

Line like point, will not be explicitly defined. As with points, we know where they are. If you think of two points, you know where the line is that contains them. The line passing through the North Pole and the South Pole is an example. The "lines" that we draw are like the "points" we draw, dark enough and wide enough so that we know where they are. As we think of lines, the ideas of "straight," "going on forever" and "containing an infinite number of points," also come to mind.

Plane:

Plane is also an undefined term. As with points, we know where they are. The plane that contains the line described above, and the center of the spot where you are seated, cuts the earth into two halves. It also divides you into two pieces and does the same thing to the universe. Whether a point is on one side of the plane, the other side of the plane, or on the plane can be determined. The "planes" that we make are like the "lines" and "points" that we draw. They are substantial enough to do what is needed. Examples of "planes" are the paper this is printed on when it is flat, walls that keep the cold away in the winter, and floors that give our students a place to stand in our classrooms. When we think of plane, the ideas of "flatness," "going on forever," "containing an infinite number of points and lines" and "infinitely thin" come to mind.

Line Segment:

A **line segment** is that part of a line that is determined by two points that is between them and includes them.

Angle:

An **angle** is the figure formed by two segments that meet at a common endpoint. This endpoint is known as the **vertex** and the segments are known as the **sides** of the angle.

Angle Measure:

Angles are measured in **degrees** (°) of rotation of the sides with respect to each other. A **360°** angle would be a complete rotation of one side, from being superimposed on the other, around to that position again. A degree is divided into 60 minutes (') and each minute is divided into 60 seconds (").

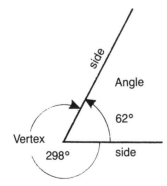

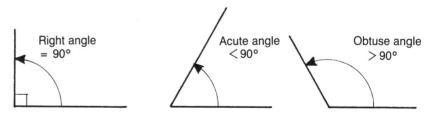

Right angle = 90°   Acute angle < 90°   Obtuse angle > 90°

Describing Angles:

A **right angle** is a quarter of a full rotation and measures **90°**; an **acute angle** measures less than (<) 90°; an **obtuse angle** measures more than (>) 90°. If the measures of two angles add to 90°, they are said to be **complementary**; if the sum is 180° they are said to be **supplementary**.

Additional Terms

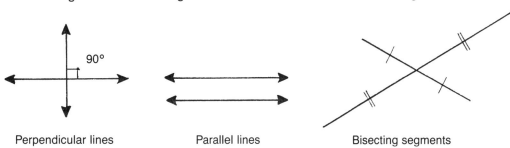

Two lines or segments **intersect** if they have one point in common. Two lines or segments are **perpendicular** if at their intersection they form right angles. Two lines are **parallel** if they are in the same plane and do not intersect. (Remember, they go on forever.) A point on a line segment will **bisect** that line segment if the two segments that are formed are the same length.

Intersecting lines   Perpendicular lines   Parallel lines   Bisecting segments

Polygon:

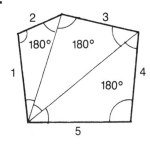

5 sides ──▶ 3 triangles

──▶ 180° + 180° + 180° = 540°
──▶ 3 x 180° = 540°
──▶ (5 - 2) x 180° = 540°

A **polygon** is a plane (flat) geometric shape bounded by 3 or more connected line segments that enclose an **interior.** The segments are called the **sides** of the polygon.

Lines have the single dimension of length, whereas polygons also have width. With the additional dimension of width, they are known as **two dimensional (2-D)** objects. The study of these objects is part of **Plane Geometry.**

The angle formed within a polygon by any two adjacent segments is an **interior** angle.

For any triangle, the sum of the interior angles is 180°.

For any polygon with n sides, the **sum of the interior angles is (n-2) x 180°.** This is equivalent to saying that n-2 non-overlapping triangles can be drawn inside.

Describing Polygons:

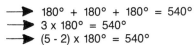

Convex polygon   Concave polygon

A polygon is **convex** if every line that passes through it intersects exactly two sides. This is equivalent to saying that all interior angles are less than 180°. A Polygon is **concave** if a line passes through it and intersects more than two sides. This is equivalent to saying that the polygon has an interior angle that is greater than 180°.

Unless specifically stated, discussions in this book will refer to convex polygons.

A polygon is **equiangular** if all interior angles have the same measure. A polygon is **equilateral** if all sides are the same length. A polygon is **regular** if it is both equiangular and equilateral.

Two polygons that have the same size and shape are said to be **congruent.** Polygons that are congruent but can only be made to look the same when viewed in a mirror, are said to be **enantiomorphic** or **handed.** Right and left footprints are natural examples of handedness. They are described as **enantiomorphs** of each other.

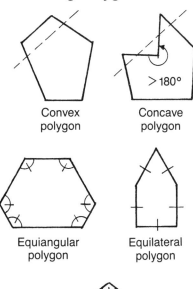

Equiangular polygon   Equilateral polygon

Regular polygon

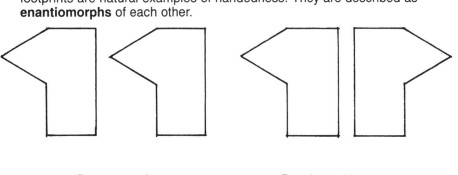

Congruent polygons   Enantiomorphic polygons

Naming Polygons

Polygons with certain numbers of sides, and therefore that many angles, have specific names. Here are some of the more common names.

In general, a polygon of n sides is referred to as an **n-gon**.

	Name of Polygon								
	triangle	quadrilateral	pentagon	hexagon	septagon	octagon	nonagon	decagon	dodecagon
Number of Sides	3	4	5	6	7	8	9	10	12

Symmetry:

Vertical line of symmetry

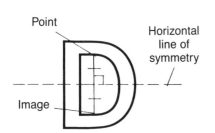

Point

Horizontal line of symmetry

Image

A figure displays **line symmetry** or **mirror symmetry** if a mirror can be placed on that line of symmetry so that the image in the mirror will be a duplicate of the shape behind the mirror, that is, every point on the figure will have a matching point on the other side of the mirror. A figure with mirror symmetry can be folded on that line and the two pieces will coincide. Examples of mirror symmetry would be the letters H, W, U, O, X, M, Y, T, I, A and V, which have a vertical line of symmetry. The letters E, O, D, H, X, C and B, have a horizontal line of symmetry.

In a figure with mirror symmetry, the line of symmetry will be the perpendicular bisector of the segment joining every point with its image.

If a figure can be rotated 360° around a center or axis, and before that rotation is over it repeats itself exactly, it is said to have **rotational symmetry**. If the image repeats **n** times during that full rotation, the figure is said to have **n-fold rotational symmetry**. The letters S, N, Z, H, X and I, have 2-fold rotational symmetry. The plus sign (+) has 4-fold rotational symmetry.

An **asymmetrical** figure like the letters G or R, will exhibit no symmetry of any kind. A figure could exhibit mirror symmetry and no rotational symmetry like the letter W, or it could have n-fold rotational symmetry and no mirror symmetry like the capital letters S, Z and N.

2-fold Rotational symmetry

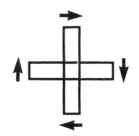

4-fold Rotational symmetry

Asymmetry

Tessellations or Tilings:

A combination of polygons **tessellates** or **tiles** a surface if it covers it completely without gaps or overlaps. In the process, they must be in the same plane or "lie flat."

Describing Tessellations:

A tessellation is said to be **uniform** if the arrangement of polygons at every vertex is identical.

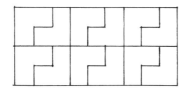

Tessellation

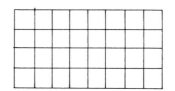

Uniform tessellation

Polygons 1

GRADES: **Kindergarten to Sixth**

GOALS: To develop the ability to duplicate a briefly viewed array of Googolplex.
To build several examples of polygons and use proper terminology.

MATERIALS: Matrix sheets.

TEACHER ACTION	STUDENT RESPONSE

During **Free Play,** be conscious of an underlying strategy to use the language of polygons in your work with the teams: **sides, angles, interior, exterior, triangle, quadrilateral, pentagon, hexagon, septagon, octagon, nonagon, decagon, dodecagon, thirteen-gon,** etc.: **convex, concave:** etc.

Bring **Free Play** to a close

Most of the important things we learn in life are copied from those around us. What can you think of that you have learned from others?

Talking, walking, making music, running, jumping, whistling, skating, riding a bike, telling time, etc.

Has anyone heard the name "copycat"? We are going to play a game that I call Copycat. I am going to show you a shape that I have made out of Googolplex. You will only see it for three seconds and then I will hide it. I want each one of you to do your best to make a copy of that shape and when you have finished, show it to me.

Their responses will vary but as you see them holding your shape, reinforce their success with an **"O.K.,"** **"That's it,"** **"You've got it,"** etc. If they are off, give them specific feedback such as **"I used three square frames,"** or **"My pieces made a corner [right angle],"** etc. For the successful ones, you might place yours on top of theirs. If later in the game the shapes are enantiomorphs of each other, point this out with a mirror, a reference to their "right and left handed nature" or the need to flip the shapes to get them to coincide.

SHOW them this shape while counting aloud "1001, 1002, 1003" then hide the shape.

Try others like these.

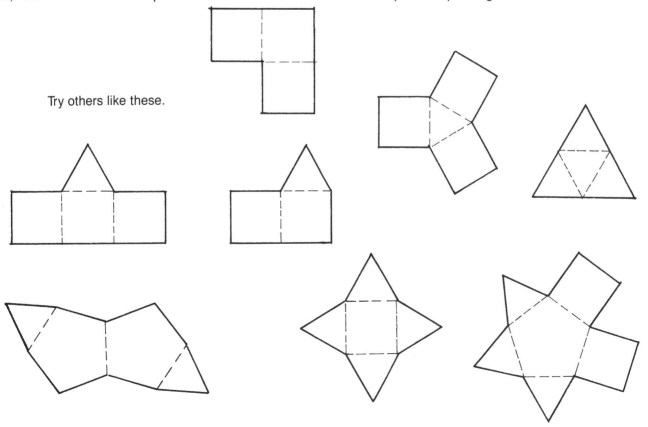

Come back to this activity often with increasingly complex displayed shapes and different viewing times as appropriate.

This will become a popular activity on subsequent days.

ASIDE: This is an important skill for such activities as reading maps, or understanding any schematic diagram.

Show them this hexagon.

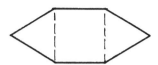

Make this shape. Who knows what it is called? Its name is based on the number of sides it has.

Discuss the meaning of "hex" and "gon," both from the Greek. The number, and the suffix for "angled."

Make some other hexagons. Imagine that each of these is a map of a piece of property. Can you take a straight walk between any two places on the property that will make you cross your neighbors land? If you can always stay on your land, it is a convex hexagon, otherwise it is concave. If it has even a shallow "cave" it is concave.

Give them a chance to challenge their classmates. However, help them to understand how very complex shapes are not a challenge as much as a "turn off" of interest in the activity.

TIP: For those who are unsuccessful, group them with a team member who is having success.

Expect a variety of answers. Look out for the correct one and latch on to it. Look for the ideas of "six sides" or "six angles." Talk of polygons and six-gons.

Help them to use the edge of a piece of paper or a ruler to find the "walk line." Share some of each type with the class.
Here are some that they might make.

TIP: Don't let them mistake a "long side" made of two Googolplex edges for two sides. It is a single side.

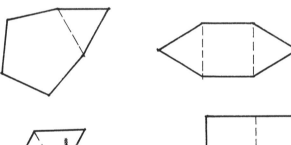

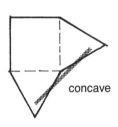
concave

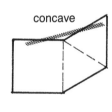
concave

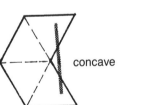
concave

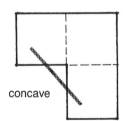
concave

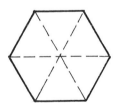

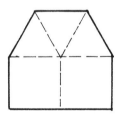

Show them a hexagonal dome.

Can you Copycat this shape? What is the name of the bottom of this dome?

Help them to make the dome shape.

Hexagon.

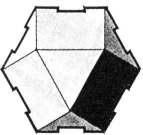

We have a word for polygons that have all the sides and angles the same size. We call them **regular**. Show me a regular hexagon. Is it concave? Why? Is the square frame regular? How about the other frames? How about the plates? How about the top of your table?

As you did with hexagons, take them through a process of making and identifying some of the other polygons, including quadrilaterals, pentagons, octagons, decagons and dodecagons. Help them find the domes that give two of the last three as regular polygons.

ASIDE: An interesting historical fact concerns the displacement of the old seventh, eighth, ninth and tenth months – September, October, November and December – to accommodate both Julius and Augustus Caesar with the insertion of both July and August.

Have them construct a matrix table with the names of the polygons down the side and these and other characteristics across the top: Number of Sides, Number of Angles, As Made with Googolplex; Convex, Concave, Regular, With 1 Piece, With 2 Pieces, As a Dome.

Try to get team members who don't often speak out, to do so. Seek explanations that go beyond "yes" and "no" answers.

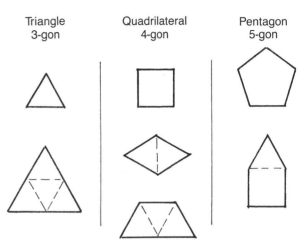

Triangle 3-gon   Quadrilateral 4-gon   Pentagon 5-gon

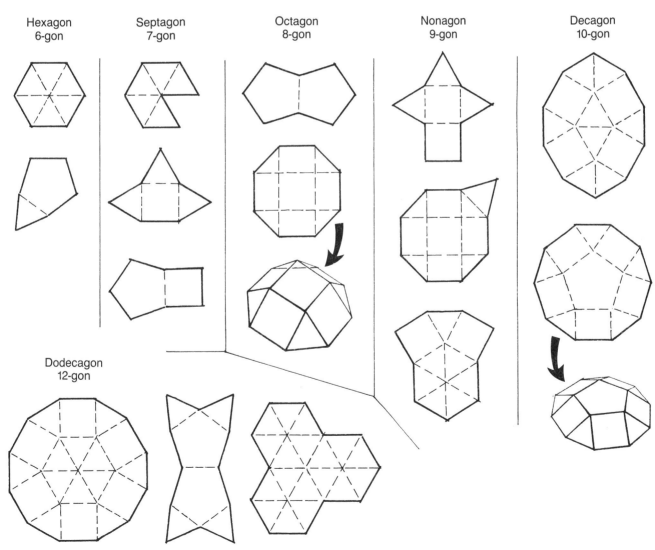

Hexagon 6-gon   Septagon 7-gon   Octagon 8-gon   Nonagon 9-gon   Decagon 10-gon

Dodecagon 12-gon

Polygons 2

GRADES: **First to Sixth**

GOALS: To develop an understanding of surrounding a point with regular polygons (tessellations).
To develop (and analyze) several schemes for covering the plane with regular polygons.

MATERIALS: A transparency of page 21 and an overhead projector.

TEACHER ACTION	STUDENT RESPONSE

During **Free Play,** build on the results of the previous sessions with the students. Continue with the measuring of their creations, working with the mirrors on symmetries, and naming the shapes in terms of the vocabulary of geometry.

Bring **Free Play** to a close

Everyone pick a frame and hold it up by a vertex. I would like you to put it down and keep track of the vertex you held. Now, connect other frames to that frame so that you surround the vertex you held. Don't leave any openings, and the final structure must lay flat.

They will have little trouble with the square and triangle. The pentagon will not work with the pieces here. Let them try, and ask what shape would be necessary to surround a pentagon's vertex. Depending on age, either accept this property of pentagons or analyze it in terms of the angles and their measure.

When polygons cover the plane like this, we say they "tessellate" or "tile" the plane.

Look for usual tessellations like 4•4•4•4 (four squares) and 3•3•3•3•3•3 (six triangles) and for less usual arrays like 3•3•4•3•4.

ASIDE: The above arrays are also written as 4^4, 3^6 and $3^2•4•3•4$. As appropriate, introduce this notation to the students and write it on the board.

Try with the regular hexagon that we made with 6 triangles. What arrays would tessellate one of its vertices?

If in POLYGONS 1 you also built the octagonal dome, the decagonal dome and the dodecagon, have them look at these regular figures for tessellating properties. (The decagon fails as did the pentagon.)

Continue to move among groups and hold up successful new arrays. Record these arrays on the board. Add 6^3, 3•4•6•4, 3•6•3•6, $3•4^2•6$, $3^2•6^2$, and $3^4•6$ to your table as they are found.

TIP: Be prepared for a discussion about different notations for the same array; it depends on where you start to write. A convention of starting with the smallest number could be followed. Also, some tessellations are mirror images of others, not different, just right and left handed ($4^2•3•6$ and $3•4^2•6$).

Show the transparency from page 21 to the students and analyze the figures with them, with respect to notation, sum of angle measures, symmetry, etc.

See that a few of the teams are working with the regular tessellations of triangles, squares and hexagons and a few are working with the other basic tiling patterns.

I would like each team to choose one of the tessellation patterns you made earlier and repeat that same pattern as you begin to cover your entire table. When a shape will cover a surface completely, we say that the shape will "tile" or "tessellate."

Move around the teams as they work to offer support and idea sharing between team efforts.

EXTENSION: There is a chance to talk about "area" here. How many square frames would it take to cover your table? Could you also use triangles and hexagons? What would be the problems in using these?

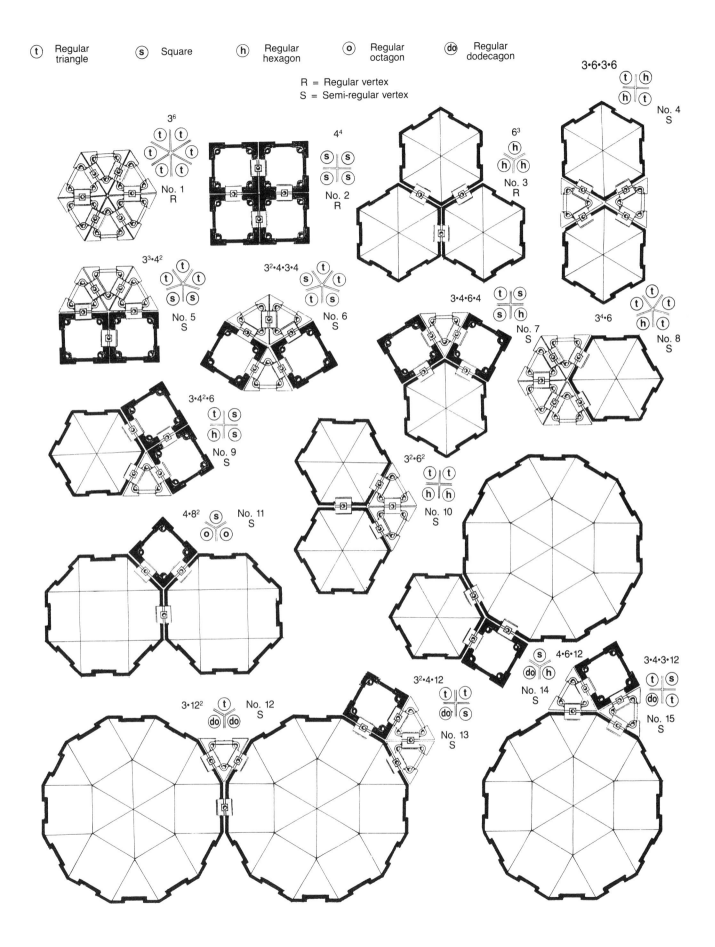

Regular triangle (t)   Square (s)   Regular hexagon (h)   Regular octagon (o)   Regular dodecagon (do)

R = Regular vertex
S = Semi-regular vertex

3^6 — No. 1 R

4^4 — No. 2 R

6^3 — No. 3 R

$3 \cdot 6 \cdot 3 \cdot 6$ — No. 4 S

$3^3 \cdot 4^2$ — No. 5 S

$3^2 \cdot 4 \cdot 3 \cdot 4$ — No. 6 S

$3 \cdot 4 \cdot 6 \cdot 4$ — No. 7 S

$3^4 \cdot 6$ — No. 8 S

$3 \cdot 4^2 \cdot 6$ — No. 9 S

$3^2 \cdot 6^2$ — No. 10 S

$4 \cdot 8^2$ — No. 11 S

$3 \cdot 12^2$ — No. 12 S

$3^2 \cdot 4 \cdot 12$ — No. 13 S

$4 \cdot 6 \cdot 12$ — No. 14 S

$3 \cdot 4 \cdot 3 \cdot 12$ — No. 15 S

I would like you to stop what you are working on now and move around the class to see the tiling patterns the other teams are making.

ASIDE: The tessellations on this page are said to be **semi-regular.** This means that all vertices have the same arrangement of polygons and any region or pattern, unrotated, (shown in gray) will repeat continuously. A **regular** tessellation is made up of polygons that are all congruent. Many of the repetitive patterns they might see are shown here.

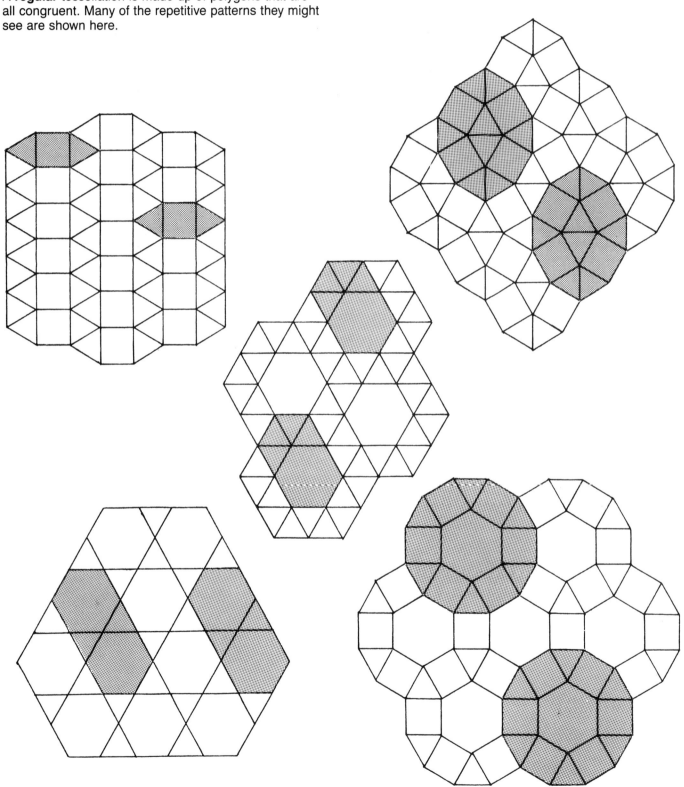

Move them back to their seats.

Sometimes patterns like those you are making are called "mosaics." Did you see any tilings that you have seen before?

They will hopefully have seen tile floors, graph paper, office ceilings, decorative mosaics, wallpaper, etc.

If a pattern could be expanded to a table top, could it cover a basketball court?

Yes, they can go on forever.

Here are some tiles that do tessellate.

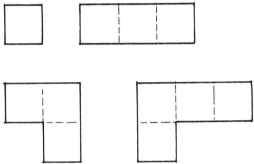

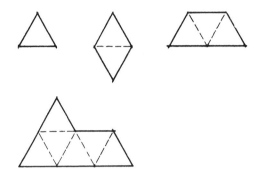

They are special though, because they can repeat and make a larger copy of themselves. Since they are repeating tiles, they are nicknamed REP-TILES. Can your team find a tiling pattern for these REP-TILES that will make them repeat?

Check to see that they maintain the same shape so that the shadow of one will fit exactly on the other.

Answers for this are shown below.

Will the same tiling plan make the larger REP-TILE repeat?

When will this stop?

When you run out of room or tiles.

How many tiles did it take?

Four or nine.

Did each REP-TILE take that number?

Yes, 4 or 9 or 16 or . . .

Can you see a pattern here?

They are square numbers

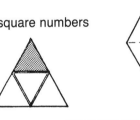

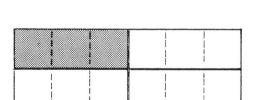

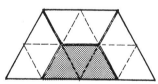

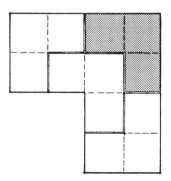

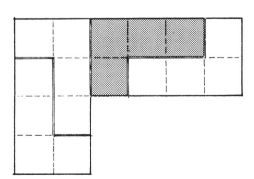

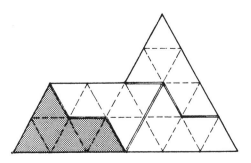

Polygons 3

GRADES: **First to Sixth**

GOALS: To develop an understanding of mirror and rotational symmetry.
           To become aware of the symmetry that surrounds us.

MATERIALS: At least two mirrors for each team, as described in Useful Tools and Techniques; page 4, unlined paper.

TEACHER ACTION	STUDENT RESPONSE

During **Free Play,** watch for the naturally occurring symmetric structures that the students make and move in with your mirrors to make the most of the opportunity.

Bring **Free Play** to a close

We are going to play a short game of Copycat.
Show these pieces.

TIP: Prepare them before class.

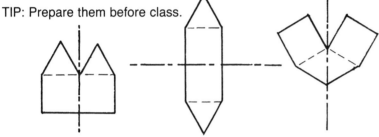

Did you notice anything about those pieces? Was there a family name for them?

Balanced, reflections, mirrors, the same on each side, folded in the middle, etc.

TIP: Heighten the impression by unfolding them on the line of symmetry as you reveal them.

They are shapes that have a mirror line on them. Who thinks they know what that might mean?

Student initiated discussion about placing a mirror on the line.

Give a student a mirror and let him show how it works. Pass mirrors out to each team and resume.

Can you always fold a Googolplex shape on a mirror line?

Answers will vary, find a student who thinks not.

Give me an example of a Googolplex shape that won't fold on a mirror line? How are they different?

Many possibilities from any of the frames to the complex shapes. "They have an odd number of pieces going cross ways."

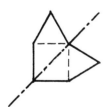 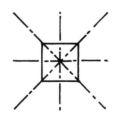

 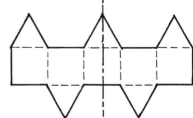

Now let's try something different. I will show you what is in front of the mirror, you show me what the entire shape might look like. Your mirror will help you see the whole shape. Choose a line, put the mirror there and then build the shape.

Here are some examples with lines of symmetry shown.

24

Show these shapes

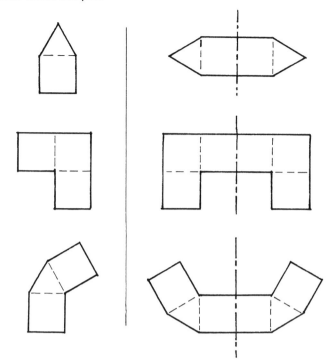

Expect these reponses

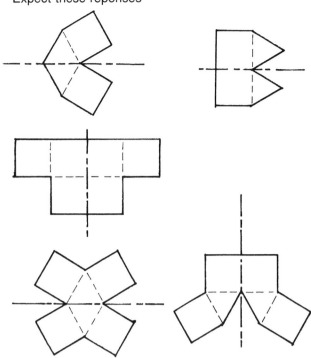

Do any of the Googolplex shapes have more than one mirror line or line of symmetry?

How many lines of symmetry does a decagon have? How about a dodecagon? How about a 20-gon? (How about a circle?)

Can you see any shapes in the room that have mirror lines or a line of symmetry?

Would you please take the piece of paper I am handing out and fold it in half. Now, by carefully tearing, with the two halves folded together, see if you have line symmetry when you open it up. Later, you might want to use a pair of scissors, make a fancier shape and color it.

For tomorrow, bring in the names of ten things in your life that have line symmetry. I will give you the first, it is the number "10." Write it so that its horizontal line of symmetry is clear.

Show them this shape that is made with same colored connectors.

Look carefully at what I am holding. When you open your eyes I want you to tell me if there has been any change. Close your eyes!

Turn the shape 180° like a propeller.

You can look.

Let half the class look while the other half can't. Again, rotate the piece and ask.

Place a plate in an end frame and try it again.

At a minimum they should see that the frames have 3, 4 and 5 respectively for the triangle, square and pentagon.

Pursue this discussion with them. Leave it with the circle having many lines of symmetry.

Many will be offered including the people themselves.

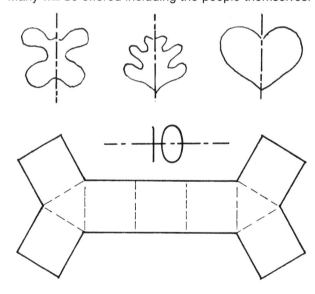

They won't be able to see any difference if you made all the connectors the same color.

Now the change is apparent.

Do the same thing with this shape.

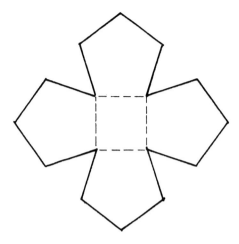

After several trials, mark an arm with a plate so that the rotation becomes clear.

How many different ways could I hold it before I put the plate in?

Four ways.

When I can rotate it to different places and you can't tell that I have, we say that is has rotational symmetry. As you look at this piece, it has 4-fold rotational symmetry. How many did the last one have?

Two.

Show me a structure that has three-fold or five-fold rotational symmetry.

Check their answers. They will be based on the triangle or pentagon.

Can you show me a structure that has two-fold rotational symmetry but no line symmetry?

It will probably be "S" or "N" like in appearance.

Show this shape.

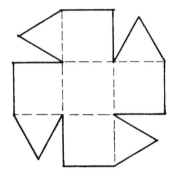

What can you tell me about the symmetries of this shape?

Four-fold rotational symmetry. No line symmetry.

What objects in our world have rotational symmetry?

They might mention some of the letters in the alphabet like S, O and H. Also flowers, ceiling fans and lamp shades. Check out their responses.

EXTENSION: If they tape their mirrors as in Useful Tools and Techniques; page 4, they can generate their own rotational symmetry with any number of folds. They become a hand held kaleidoscope. Have them write up a brief explanation of what they did and include sketches.

©1988 ARLINGTON-HEWS, INC. investigating POLYGONS and POLYHEDRA with Googolplex®

Polyhedra
Vocabulary and Concepts

Polyhedron:

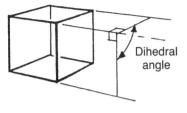

Dihedral angle

A **polyhedron** (pl. polyhedra or polyhedrons) is a geometric "solid" with **faces** (surfaces) that are polygons. The interior of a polyhedron is bounded so that you can not move to the exterior without passing through a face.

Polyhedra build on the two dimensional (2-D) nature of polygons, often labeled length and width, with the third dimension of height, therefore they are described as **three dimensional (3-D)**. The study of these objects is part of **Solid Geometry**.

Every two adjacent polygonal faces share a common line segment or **edge** and form a **dihedral angle** with respect to each other. The dihedral angle is measured in degrees in the plane that is perpendicular to its edge.

The point where three or more edges intersect is known as a **vertex.**

Describing Polyhedra:

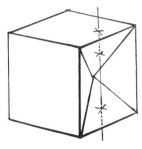

Concave polyhedron

A polyhedron is **convex** if every line segment that connects points on different faces is in the interior of the polyhedron. This is equivalent to saying that every interior dihedral angle measures less than 180°.

A polyhedron is **concave** if there is a line segment connecting points on different faces that is in the exterior of the polygon. This is equivalent to saying that at least one interior dihedral angle measures more than 180°, or that one exterior dihedral angle measures less than 180°.

The sum of the measures of all the face angles at a vertex in a convex polyhedron will always be less than 360°.

A polyhedron is **uniform** if all of its vertices are congruent, i.e. the type and order of the polygons meeting at each vertex and their dihedral angles are the same.

A polyhedron is **regular** if it is uniform and all faces are only one type of congruent regular polygon. All dihedral angles are also congruent. There are only five regular polyhedra. They have 4, 6, 8, 12 and 20 faces.

With the exception of the cube (6 faces), the regular polyhedra follow the naming scheme laid out in the table below. They are called the **Platonic Solids** because of their importance in the work of the Greek philosopher Plato.

Naming Polyhedra:

One labeling scheme for polyhedra is dependent on the number of faces. The label combines a Greek or Latin based prefix that indicates a number, with the suffix "hedron" meaning side or face. Here is a less than comprehensive list with more labels than you will probably ever need.

In general, a polyhedron with n sides is called an **n-hedron.**

It must be noted that many of the polyhedra have torturous labels that may relate to the formation of the solid instead of the number of sides. Some have two or more different names.

Number of faces	Name of Polyhedron
4	Tetrahedron
5	Pentahedron
6	Hexahedron
7	Septahedron
8	Octahedron
10	Decahedron
12	Dodecahedron
14	Tetrakaidecahedron
15	Pentakaidecahedron
16	Hexakaidecahedron
20	Icosahedron
26	Icosihexahedron
32	Icosidodecahedron

Symmetry:

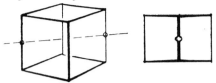

(a) Edge symmetry (2-fold)

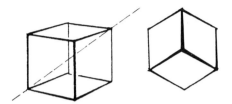

(b) Vertex symmetry (3-fold)

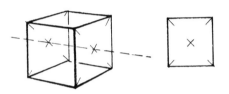

(c) Face symmetry (4-fold)

The 3 orientations of symmetry for a cube

Euler's Theorem for Polyhedra:

Prisms:

Pyramids:

Nets:

Duals:

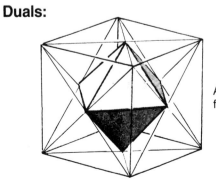

An octahedron formed from a cube

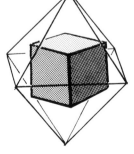

A cube formed from an octahedron

Polyhedra, like polygons can exhibit mirror symmetry and n-fold rotational symmetry.

A polyhedron or any 3-D structure displays **mirror symmetry** with respect to a plane if a mirror could replace that plane and the image in the mirror would appear the same as the hidden part of the polygon. Every point in front of the plane (vertices, points on a line or points in a plane) will be present in the image. Also, the line segments joining points with their images will be bisected by the plane and be perpendicular to it.

A polyhedron or 3-D structure displays **n-fold rotational symmetry** if it repeats itself exactly **n** times in a full rotation about an **axis.** The axis on which a polyhedron will turn as it demonstrates n-fold rotational symmetry will either enter at a vertex, at the center of an edge, or at the center of a face.

The cube pictured at the side shows rotational symmetry with respect to three axes, 2-fold with respect to the center of an edge, 3-fold with respect to a vertex and 4-fold with respect to a face. It is said to belong to the **2-3-4 symmetry family.**

In this exploration of polyhedra we will be working with the 5 Platonic solids and the 13 Archimedian solids. With the exception of the tetrahedron, and the truncated tetrahedron they all belong to the **2-3-4 symmetry family** or the **2-3-5 symmetry family.** The tetrahedron and the truncated tetrahedron with two types of rotational symmetry, belongs to the **2-3 symmetry family.**

A polyhedron or three dimensional structure may have no symmetry at all, in which case it is described as **asymmetric.** If a solid displays symmetry, it may be present in any combination of rotational and mirror symmetries.

F + V = E + 2 is the relation between the number of faces (F) of a polyhedron, its vertices (V) and its edges (E). It says that the total number of faces and vertices of a polyhedron is 2 more than the number of edges. This relation was discovered by Leonhard Euler, hence its name.

A **prism** is a polyhedron with two parallel and congruent polygonal faces **(bases)** that have the same orientation, and that are connected with parallelograms. If the parallelograms are rectangles the figure is a **right prism.** If all the polygons are regular it is a **semi-regular prism.** The cube could be described as a, "semi-regular square prism."

A **pyramid** is a solid formed by combining a polygonal base and triangular sides that meet at a vertex. It is called a **regular pyramid** if the base polygon is regular and all the triangles are congruent. They are named after their base, for example a triangular pyramid would have a triangle for a base.

If enough of the edges of a polyhedron are separated so that the all of its faces can be laid flat, the resultant arrangement of connected polygons is called a **net** for that polyhedron.

Two regular (Platonic) polyhedra are said to be **duals** if one could be formed by connecting the center-points of the adjacent faces of the other.

Polyhedra 1

GRADES: **Second to Sixth**

GOALS: To extend an initial understanding of the structural and symmetrical nature of polyhedra by creating and analyzing the Platonic solids.

MATERIALS: Matrix sheets, graph paper.

TEACHER ACTION	STUDENT RESPONSE

A large amount of unstructured investigation with Googolplex must occur on the part of the children if they are to be ready for this and later work. Making space stations, modern houses, floor tile designs and other self-identified projects will allow them to see the possibilities and limitations of the material and the shapes in a way that directed lessons rarely do. Time invested here will pay large dividends. During **Free Play,** focus attention on the solid structures that the students are making. Pay attention to using the language of solid geometry including the names of the various polyhedra: **tetrahedron, cube (hexahedron), octahedron, dodecahedron, icosahedron** among the others; and their parts and properties: **face, vertex, edge, pyramid, prism, convex, concave,** and the types of **symmetry.**

Bring **Free Play** to a close

Make this shape.

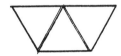

Have them describe the shape.

Three triangles in a line, quadrilateral, half a hexagon, etc.

Keep that shape and make this.

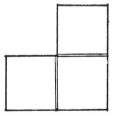

Have them describe this shape and how it is like the other.

Three squares in an "L," three quarters of a square, three squares starting to **tessellate** around a point. They both have three. They are both trying to wrap around a common **vertex** but they don't make it.

Keep those two shapes in front of you and do the same thing with pentagonal frames.

Keep the considerations of "three-ness" and "common vertex" before them.

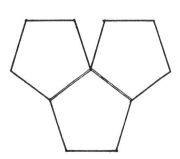

Can you connect the three triangles into a tent shape?	Yes.
Can you do it with the three squares?	It looks more like a roof.
Can you do that with the pentagons?	Yes, it also looks like a roof.
Save your "roof" and "tent" shapes.	They should have these shapes.

Will four pentagons around a vertex make a roof shape?	No, not like the others.
How about four squares?	They would keep the rain off but there is no room underneath. They are flat. They tessellate. They aren't forced to stand in a roof shape.
Will four triangles around a vertex rise off the table?	Yes, it looks like a tent.
Put it with the other roofs. Would five pentagons or squares work?	No.
How about five triangles around a vertex?	Yes.
Put them with the other roof-like shapes you are saving. **Do six triangles work? Why?**	No. They have the same problem as four squares.
How many shapes do you have in your collection? Can you put them in families?	Five. Three frame, four frame and five frame family. Triangle, square and pentagon family.
Is there a two piece family? Show me.	No. They would fold against each other.
As a team, choose one of your shapes. Can you connect more of the same frame to the "roof" to make a polyhedron? Do this so that every vertex has the same pattern.	Drawings and nets of the **Platonic Solids** are on pages 31 and 32.

Have the teams compare their efforts and make themselves a complete set of the Platonic Solids.	Move among the teams and insert vocabulary, encouragement and guidance as it is appropriate.

EXTENSION: Do a short historical on the Platonic Solids, and their importance to Plato.

Pass out matrix paper and have them make a chart with the shape composition down the side and the characteristics across the top.

On side: FRAMES AT EACH VERTEX: 3 triangles, 4 triangles, 5 triangles, 3 squares, 3 pentagons.

As evidence accumulates, discuss the special nature of the Platonic Solids (regular polyhedra) with the students.

Across top: CHARACTERISTIC: number of frames **(faces)** in finished shape, name of finished shape, number of **edges,** number of **vertices,** and other characteristics they choose.

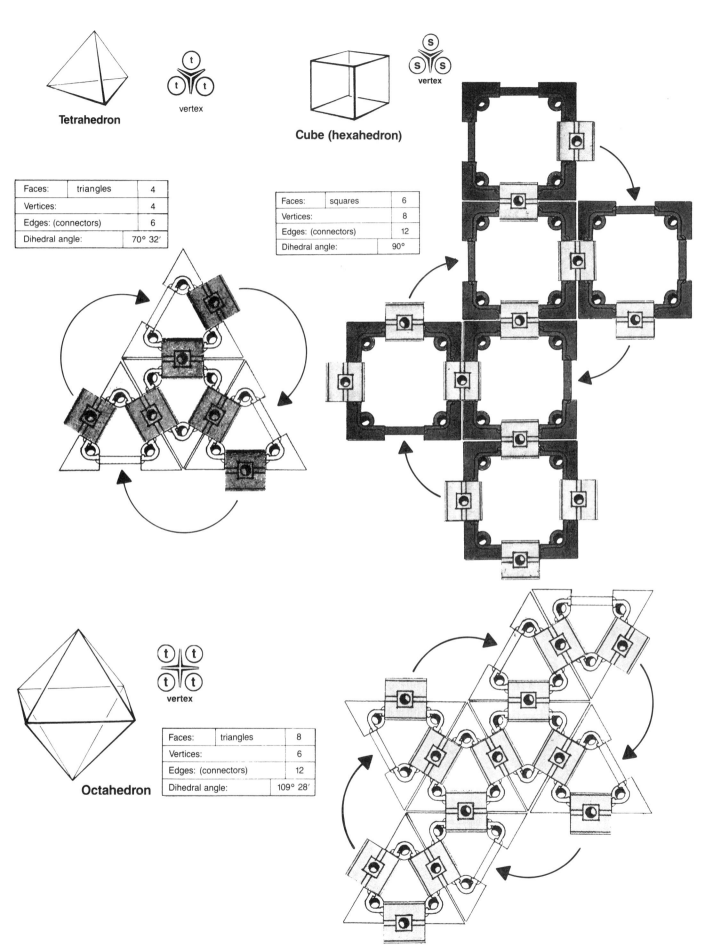

Tetrahedron

Faces:	triangles	4
Vertices:		4
Edges: (connectors)		6
Dihedral angle:		70° 32′

Cube (hexahedron)

Faces:	squares	6
Vertices:		8
Edges: (connectors)		12
Dihedral angle:		90°

Octahedron

Faces:	triangles	8
Vertices:		6
Edges: (connectors)		12
Dihedral angle:		109° 28′

vertex

vertex

Dodecahedron

Faces:	pentagons	12
Vertices:		20
Edges: (connectors)		30
Dihedral angle:		116° 34′

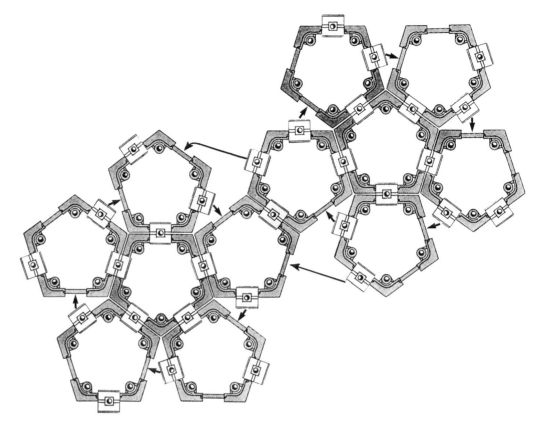

vertex

Icosahedron

Faces:	triangles	20
Vertices:		12
Edges: (connectors)		30
Dihedral angle:		138° 11′

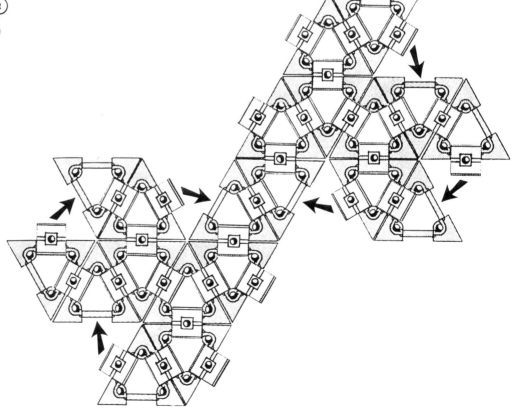

Copycat this shape.

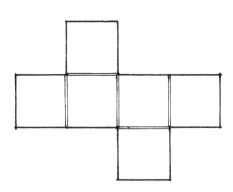

Can you fold this net and connect it so that it becomes a cube?

Can you find different nets that will fold into a cube?

Let them find that there are ten more. Don't set ten as a goal or a limit. Don't show all possibilities unless they have stalled and you won't be able to come back to this.

Pass out graph paper and have them sketch their nets on the graph paper.

You might also have them draw a dotted line on any **lines of symmetry** and an "x" on any **axes of rotational symmetry.** Post their work.

EXTENSION: Apply this same process to the other Platonic solids.

They should have little trouble.

There are ten more. Move among the working teams acknowledging new ones as they appear. Help them to see **mirror** and **rotational symmetry** in the nets. Point out right and left handed nets **(enantiomorphs)** that are really the same. Display new nets at the front of the class.

TIP: Have them approach in a methodical way by finding all that have exactly four in a row, then exactly three in a row, and lastly, no more than two in a row.

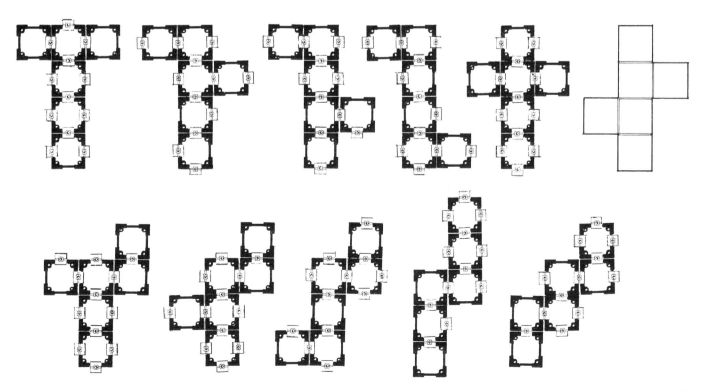

Polyhedra 2

GRADES: **Second to Sixth**

GOALS: To gain a further understanding of the geometry of polyhedra by constructing and analyzing some pyramids and prisms.

MATERIALS: At least two camping mirrors per team and a taped pair for the teacher (see Useful Tools and Techniques, p. 4), protractors, matrix sheets.

TEACHER ACTION	STUDENT RESPONSE

During **Free Play,** encourage the making of the Platonic Solids that were made in the previous lesson and variations on those structures. With mirrors (two mirrors center hinged if possible) move among the teams and respond to the structures that are being made in terms of demonstrable symmetry. Reinforce the language and concept of **face, edge** and **vertex**, and use the language of **dihedral angle.** If the 11 nets for the cube haven't all been displayed, encourage additional efforts.

Bring **Free Play** to a close

Please Copycat this net.

Fold it into a polyhedron and connect the edges.

TIP: Make yours with one color connector for later symmetry use.

Have you seen this shape before?

Yes. In Egypt, toys, etc.

What was it called?

A **pyramid.**

How is this pyramid like a cube.

It is built on a square base.

This is called a square pyramid.

What shape are its sides?

Triangles.

All pyramids have triangular sides that meet at a single vertex.

Save the square pyramid and build pyramids on the triangle and the pentagon.

What other name did we give to the triangular pyramid?

Tetrahedron. Move around to see they understand and are having success.

EXTENSION: Try to make a hexagonal pyramid and discuss the problem of triangles that are too short and a "roof" that won't rise above the base.

Take the square pyramid and place your mirror in the slot that is formed on the top. What do you see in the mirror as you adjust it?

The other side of the pyramid.

Remove the two connectors that the mirror is resting on so it rests on the base. Is the picture better?

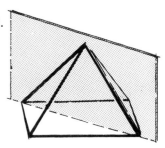

Pyramids and Dipyramids

ASIDE: An interesting figure related to the **pyramid** is the **dipyramid.** It consists two congruent pyramids on opposite sides of a shared base.

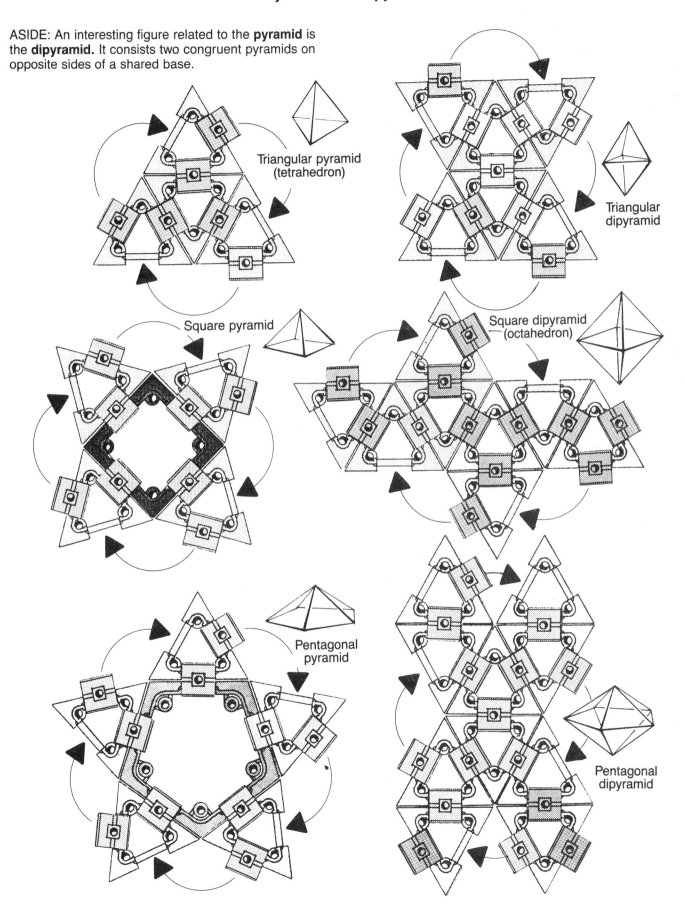

Triangular pyramid
(tetrahedron)

Triangular
dipyramid

Square pyramid

Square dipyramid
(octahedron)

Pentagonal
pyramid

Pentagonal
dipyramid

If the mirror could slice through the square pyramid like a hot knife slices through butter, where else could we put it to show symmetry.

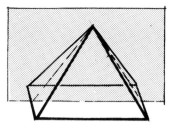

What did the one mirror do with the triangles that were in front of it?

It doubled them, copied them, etc.

With the technique of **Polygons 3**, page 25 and 26, or in some other way, let them find the 4-fold symmetry of the square pyramid about the axis through the center of the base and the vertex.

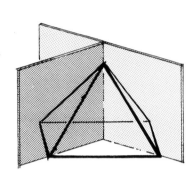

Put the mirror back in the slot in the top of the pyramid. Now, remove the connector in front of the mirror that holds the two triangle frames together. Take your second mirror and put it in this new slot and let it touch the other mirror like the walls of a room meeting in a corner.

Does anything happen as you look into both mirrors?

You still see the whole pyramid.

If you took off all the triangles behind the mirrors, would you still see the whole pyramid when you look between the mirrors?

Yes.

What do the two mirrors with this angle do to the one triangle in front of them?

Make it repeat 3 more times so you can see 4.

It seems like it is related to 4-fold symmetry because it is repeated 4 times around the circle.

Encourage their response to this observation. If time allows go on to the extension.

EXTENSION: Attach two mirrors at the edge with a tape hinge as in **Polygons 3,** and use them with the **triangular pyramid** and the **pentagonal pyramid** by removing the connectors so that the mirrors will slide down to the base between the frames. See what the relation is between the **dihedral angle** and the number of repetitions of the pattern.

Let's change pace. Make this.

I would like you to Copycat the dihedral angle I set between these two square frames.

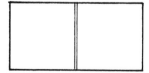

Show dihedral angles of many sizes from about 45° to 180°. As they copy, slowly open them from fully closed (0°) to open flat (180°) and then close them again while you state verbally the approximate angle measure on the way open, "**15°, 30°, 60°, here comes 90°,**" etc., and have them say the measure on the way back.

Pass out protractors.

Copy this dihedral angle and measure it. (Show them about 135°.)

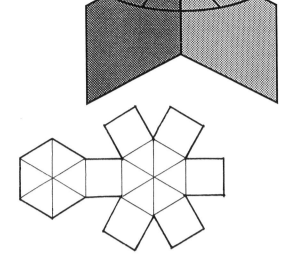

Show me a dihedral angle with a measure of 90°, 45°, ¼ of a whole circle, ½ of a whole circle.

Use your protractor and measure the dihedral angle between the two mirrors we used on the square pyramid. What is it?

90°

This dihedral angle activity needs more time than indicated here.

Let's shift gears again. Please copy this net and turn it into a polyhedron.

See that the top and bottom (the bases) are hexagons and flat.

Do you know the name of a shape like this?

Wheel, among others.

What word will the name contain?

Hexagon or hexagonal.

Shapes like this are called prisms so this is a hexagonal prism. Can you describe this prism?

The top and bottom are the same and the sides are squares.

As it turns out, the sides only have to be rectangles but squares will do.

Make some other prisms based on the triangle, square, pentagon and some non-regular polygons.

Move around as they are working and ask for the names of the various shapes – **pentagonal prism, square prism, triangular prism.**

What does most of the world call a square prism?

A cube.

Measure the dihedral angle between the square frames on the hexagonal prism. How large is it?

About 120°. Help them to place the protractor on the top of the prism and align it so that the angle can be read.

Measure the dihedral angles on the other prisms and fill in a matrix sheet with your results.

On side: POLYGON TYPE: Triangular Prism, Square Prism, Pentagonal Prism, Hexagonal Prism.

Across top: DIHEDRAL ANGLE SIZE: Base Polygon to Side, Side to Side.

Using similar techniques to those above, help them to discover the symmetries of the prisms. The hexagonal prism works well for this because you can remove the connectors and actually insert the mirrors. Do not let them forget the plane through the middle of the sides. Extend the matrix sheet headings across the top to include: Number of Mirror Symmetry Planes, Degree (n) of Rotational Symmetry.

EXTENSIONS:
1) Have them invent a way to measure the angles on the pyramids they made before and enter that information on a matrix along with the symmetry data.
2) Build a second investigation based on dipyramids and antiprisms (see pages 35 and 38).
TIP: Help them to discover a way to transfer the angle to the two square frames we used earlier so that they can measure the angle between the planes of that device.

Prisms and Antiprisms

ASIDE: A variation on the **prism** is the **antiprism** which has triangular sides and parallel congruent polygonal bases (faces).

Note: A square prism is a cube and a triangular antiprism is an octahedron

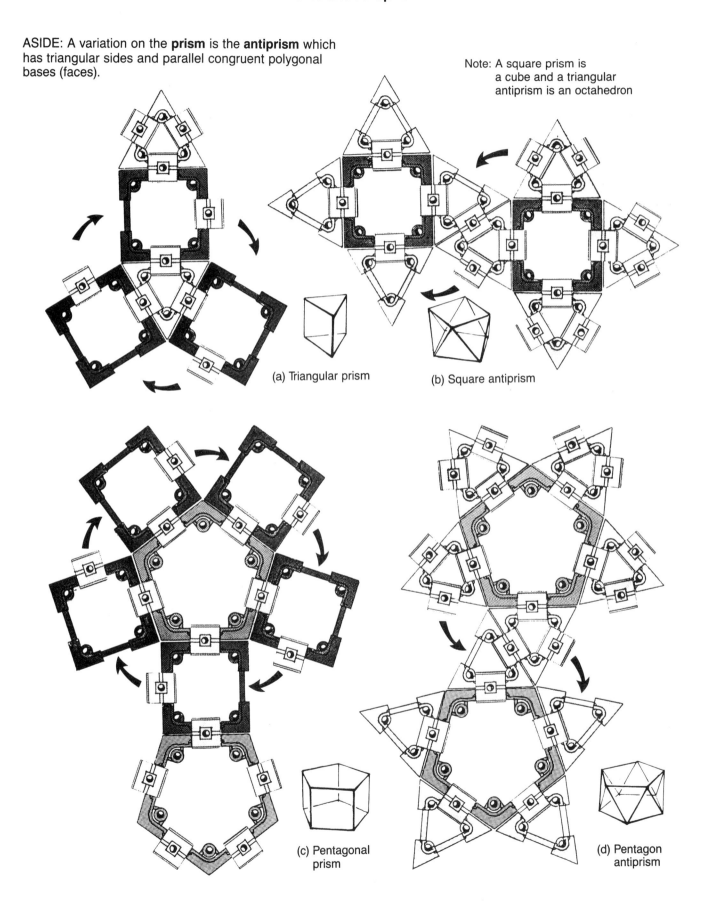

(a) Triangular prism

(b) Square antiprism

(c) Pentagonal prism

(d) Pentagon antiprism

Polyhedra 3

GRADES: **Second to Sixth**

GOALS: To analyze Platonic polyhedra in terms of vertices, edges and faces (Euler's theorem) and symmetry. To discover relationships between Platonic Solids paired as duals.

MATERIALS: Matrix transparency and overhead projector, two mirrors for each team.

TEACHER ACTION	STUDENT RESPONSE
During **Free Play,** continue reinforcing the **symmetry** concepts and the proper use of vocabulary as you recognize the interesting forms that the students are creating. Keep using the words **polyhedra, face, edge, vertex, dihedral angle, prism, pyramid.**	
Bring **Free Play** to a close	
Would you please use four triangular frames and make the top of a square pyramid for your team.	Watch that they do not put the base in place.
Now, I would like you to place it on top of a mirror and notice the shape that you appear to have. How many faces does it have?	Eight.
Do you recall what we call that figure?	An octahedron.
It is also called a square dipyramid and we saw it in the last section. Can you figure out where this name might come from?	It looks like two square pyramids put together and "di" often means two like in **di**alogue (two people talking), **di**hedral (two planes), **di**oxide (two oxygen atoms).
Take some more triangles and finish making the octahedron.	Move around as they work.
Can you remember all the arrangements of polygon frames that we used at each vertex when we made the Platonic polyhedra?	3 triangles, 4 triangles, 5 triangles, 3 squares, 3 pentagons.
Build the polyhedra that we made with these arrangements at each vertex.	TIP: Unless each team has a full set of Googolplex, they will not have enough triangles or pentagons to make all these shapes and will have to either combine teams or make less than the complete set and share information.
How many faces do they have	Four, six, eight, twelve, twenty.
Can you remember the prefixes for these n-hedra?	**Tetra**hedron, cube (**hexa**hedron), **octa**hedron, **dodeca**hedron, **icosa**hedron.
These shapes all have very regular features. How might we describe them by using the words "all the same?"	The **faces** are **all the same.** The number and kind of angles at each **vertex** are all the same. The **dihedral angles** at the **edges** are **all the same.**
TIP: Get them to recall the adjective **regular** used with polygons and its meaning that all angles and sides were the same or **congruent.** Tell them the same word applies to polyhedra.	

How many faces, vertices and edges are there for each shape. Let's make a matrix to keep track of that information. I will keep one on the overhead and you keep one for your team.

(Photo-reduced copy of matrix table.)

ATTRIBUTE

PLATONIC POLYHEDRON	Regular	Number of Faces	Number of Vertices	Number of Edges
Tetrahedron	Y	4	4	6
Cube (Hexahedron)	Y	6	8	12
Octahedron	Y	8	6	12
Dodecahedron	Y	12	20	30
Icosahedron	Y	20	12	30

Table 4

Do you see any patterns in the table? What are they?

The cube and octahedron have the same number of edges (12) and so do the icosahedron and the dodecahedron (30). The face numbers and the vertex numbers on these pairs are just reversed. The numbers on the tetrahedron aren't like any others. The number of faces and vertices always seem to be two more than the number of edges.

Will this work on other polyhedra?

Write their responses on the board.

TIP: Give each team a named shape and have them check it out. Some possible shapes are any of the pyramids, dipyramids, prisms or antiprisms made last time.

This relationship was noticed two thousand years ago, but was named for Leonard Euler ("oiler") who worked with it in the 1700's. Euler's Theorem states that F + V = E + 2.

Write it on the board.

Let's change pace for a while. I would like to take a look at any symmetry that is here. Let us just look at the cube. What symmetries did you find?

They will see many planes of mirror symmetry.

Can you demonstrate those symmetries by touching the edge of the mirror to the cube and adjusting it, or by inserting the corner of the mirror into the space between two frames on that plane? Remember what you see in the mirror must look like what is hidden by the mirror except for color.

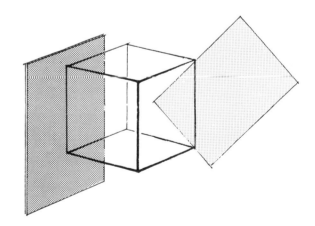

Do you find any rotational symmetry? Where are the axes of rotation?

They will be able to demonstrate the axes but will probably be at a loss for words to describe them.

Help them with the words.

You mean through the center of the face (center of the edge, vertex)? So you have a face centered, edge centered, vertex centered axis of symmetry. How many times does the cube repeat in one rotation when you turn it on that axis?"

Show them how to insert rods in the centers of the two face plates or edges. The vertex centered axis can be located by inserting 2 rods through the vertices (this must be done from the inside) and connecting them in the center of the cube with a triangular plate.

Stick with this until they find the 3-fold rotational symmetry axis through opposite vertices, the 2-fold rotational symmetry axis through opposite edge centers, and 4-fold rotational symmetry axis through opposite face centers.

Let's enter that information on our attribute matrix. Label three more of your columns "Edge Centered Rotational," "Vertex Centered Rotational" and "Face Centered Rotational."

TIP: Have them review their results and enter the data (2, 3, 4) in the table.

Go through this process again with the octahedron and enter that information (2, 4, 3) in the table.

If time allows, or on another day, determine the symmetries of the icosahedron and the dodecahedron and enter that in the table.

Does anyone see a relationship between these numbers?

ASIDE: Some solids may not display all three types of rotational symmetry, (edge, vertex, face centered) but their fold numbers will be listed in numerical order. With the dodecahedron/icosahedron pair, the cube/octahedron situation is mimicked but the symmetries are 2, 3, 5.

The cube and octahedron seem to be related in two ways, 1) through faces, vertices, and edges and 2) through symmetries. Let us look a little further.

Each team; take your cube and octahedron and put plates in all the frames and put rods in the centers of each of those plates. Now, compare these two shapes. What do you notice?

Do these rods let you see each shape in the other?

What is happening with these two polyhedra?

When two polyhedra seem to be married like this, we use the word duals to describe them. We say the cube and the octahedron are duals of each other.

Have them finish the attribute matrix and see if the icosahedron and the dodecahedron are duals.

EXTENSION: On the following pages there are nets for the Archimedean Polyhedra. Let the students build these, look at their compliance with Euler's theorem, their symmetric properties and their duals. They should also be encouraged to try to find other polyhedra and to analyze them. This would make a good science fair theme. Some of the books in the bibliography devote sections to these solids, and would provide a fascinating guide for interested students.

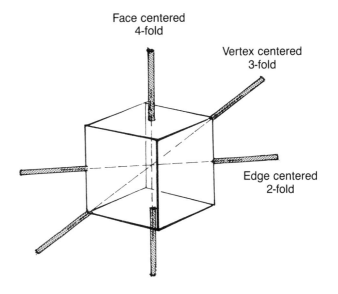

Face centered
4-fold

Vertex centered
3-fold

Edge centered
2-fold

Yes, they behave like the numbers for faces, vertices and edges, same numbers, different order.

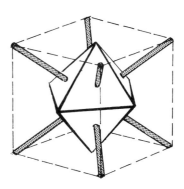

They seem to be one inside the other, etc.

vertex

Truncated tetrahedron

Faces:	hexagons	4
	triangles	4
Vertices:		12
Edges:		18
Dihedral angles:	h-h	70° 32'
	t-h	109° 28'

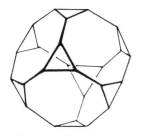

vertex

Truncated cube

Faces:	triangles	8
	octagons	6
Vertices:		24
Edges:		36
Dihedral angles:	o-t	125° 16'
	o-o	90°

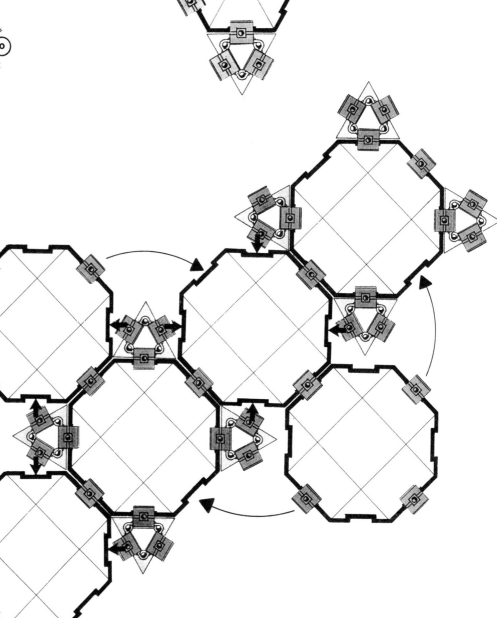

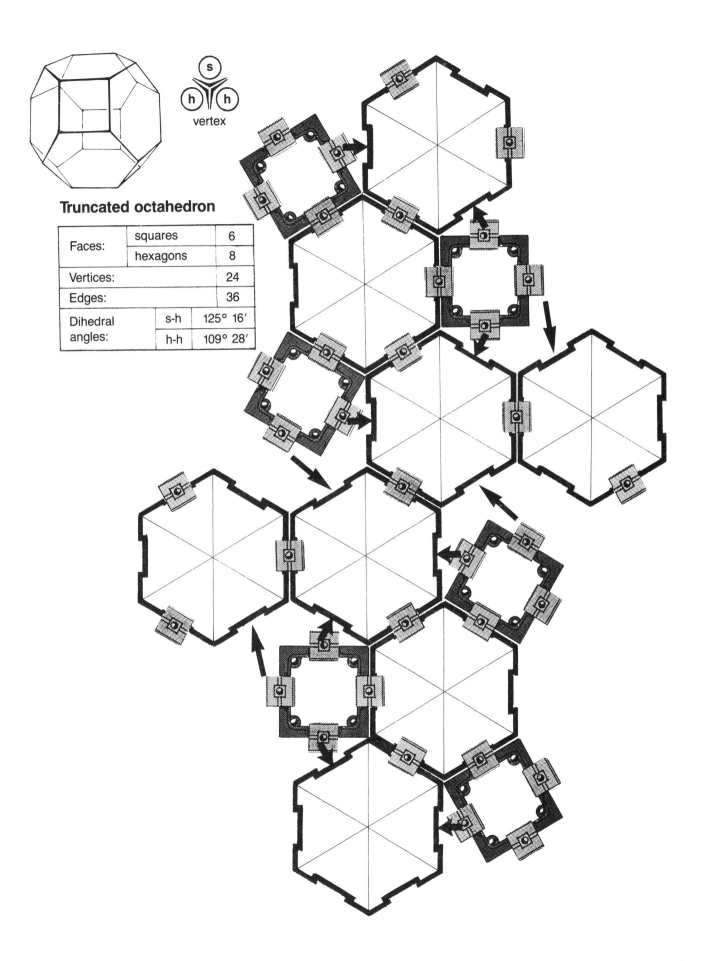

Truncated octahedron

Faces:	squares	6
	hexagons	8
Vertices:		24
Edges:		36
Dihedral angles:	s-h	125° 16′
	h-h	109° 28′

vertex

Truncated dodecahedron

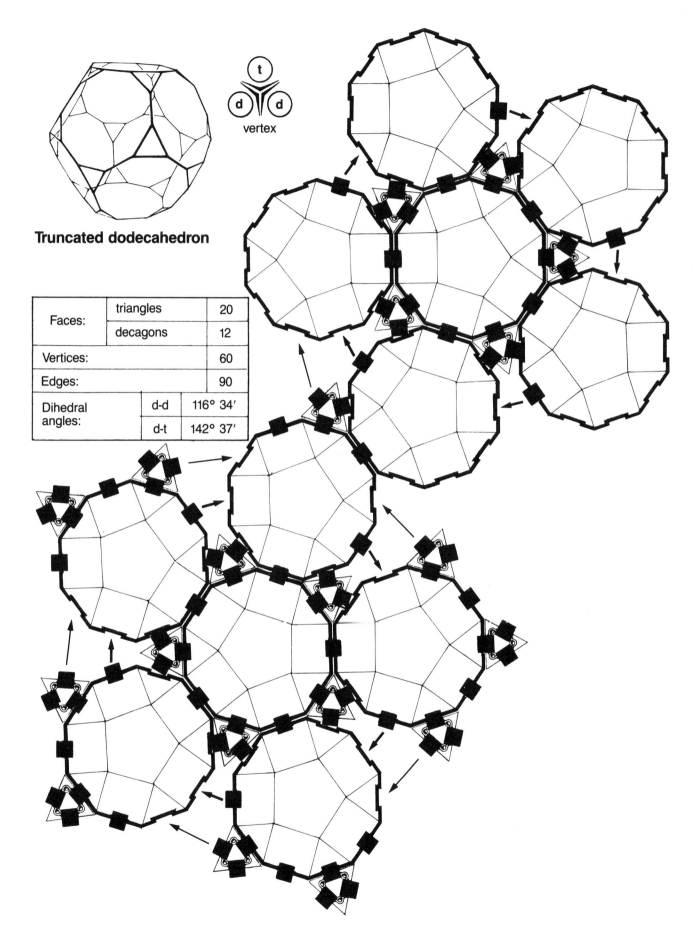

Faces:	triangles	20
	decagons	12
Vertices:		60
Edges:		90
Dihedral angles:	d-d	116° 34′
	d-t	142° 37′

vertex

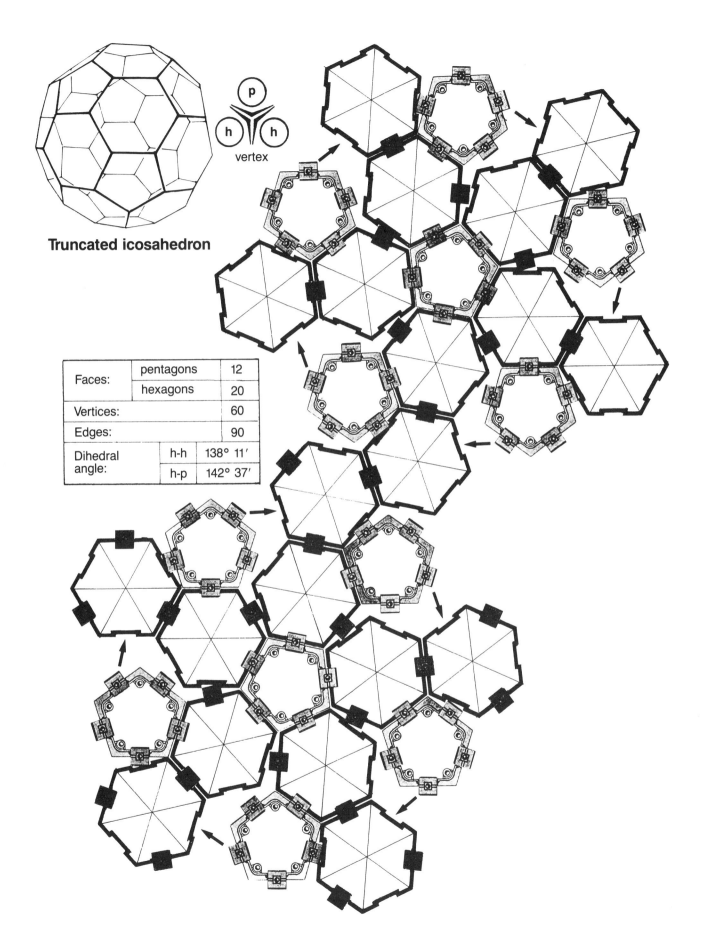

Truncated icosahedron

vertex

Faces:	pentagons	12
	hexagons	20
Vertices:		60
Edges:		90
Dihedral angle:	h-h	138° 11′
	h-p	142° 37′

vertex

Cuboctahedron

Faces:	triangles	8
	squares	6
Vertices:		12
Edges: (connectors)		24
Dihedral angle:		125° 16′

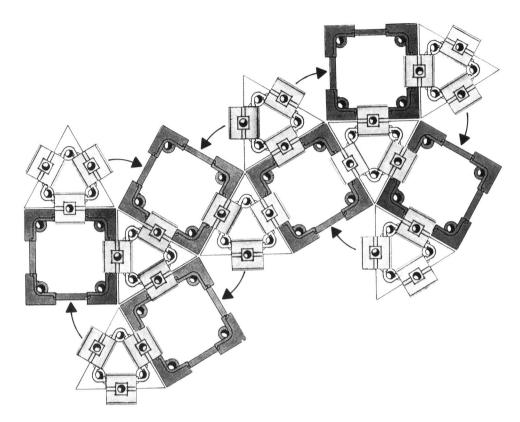

vertex

Faces:	triangles	20
	pentagons	12
Vertices:		30
Edges: (connectors)		60
Dihedral angle:		142° 37′

Icosidodecahedron

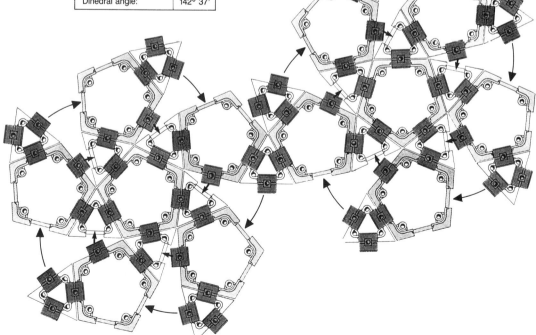

vertex

Faces:	triangles	32
	squares	6
Vertices:		24
Edges: (connectors)		60
Dihedral angles:	s-t	142° 59′
	t-t	153° 14′

Snub cuboctahedron or snub cube
(enantiomorphic; left handed form shown)

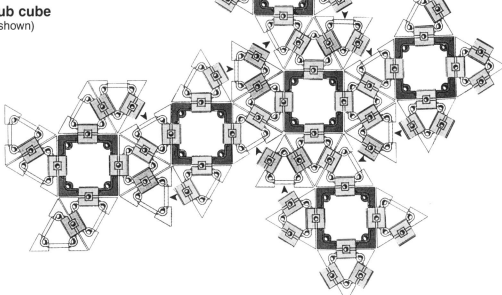

vertex

Faces:	triangles	80
	pentagons	12
Vertices:		60
Edges: (connectors)		150
Dihedral angles:	p-t	152° 56′
	t-t	164° 11′

Snub icosidodecahedron or snub dodecahedron
(enantiomorphic;
right handed form shown)

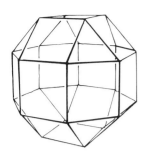

Rhombicuboctahedron

vertex

Faces:	triangles	8
	squares	18
Vertices:		24
Edges: (connectors)		48
Dihedral angles:	s-s	135°
	s-t	144° 44'

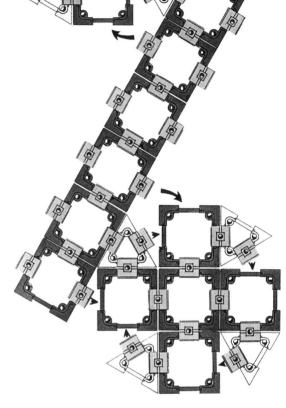

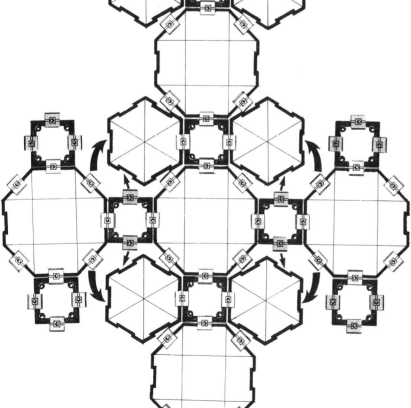

Truncated cuboctahedron or greater rhombicuboctahedron

Faces:	squares	12
	hexagons	8
	octagons	6
Vertices:		48
Edges:		72
Dihedral angles:	o-s	135°
	o-h	125° 16'
	h-s	144° 44'

Truncated icosidodecahedron or greater rhombicosidodecahedron

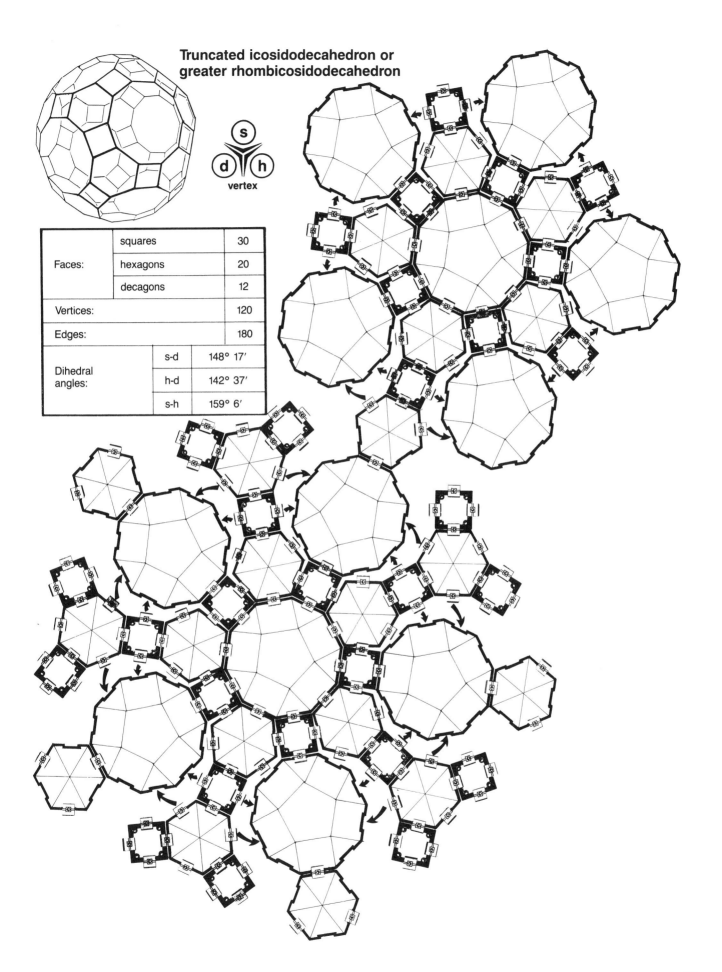

Faces:	squares	30
	hexagons	20
	decagons	12
Vertices:		120
Edges:		180
Dihedral angles:	s-d	148° 17′
	h-d	142° 37′
	s-h	159° 6′

Faces:	triangles	20
	squares	30
	pentagons	12
Vertices:		60
Edges: (connectors)		120
Dihedral angles:	p-s	148° 17′
	t-s	159° 6′

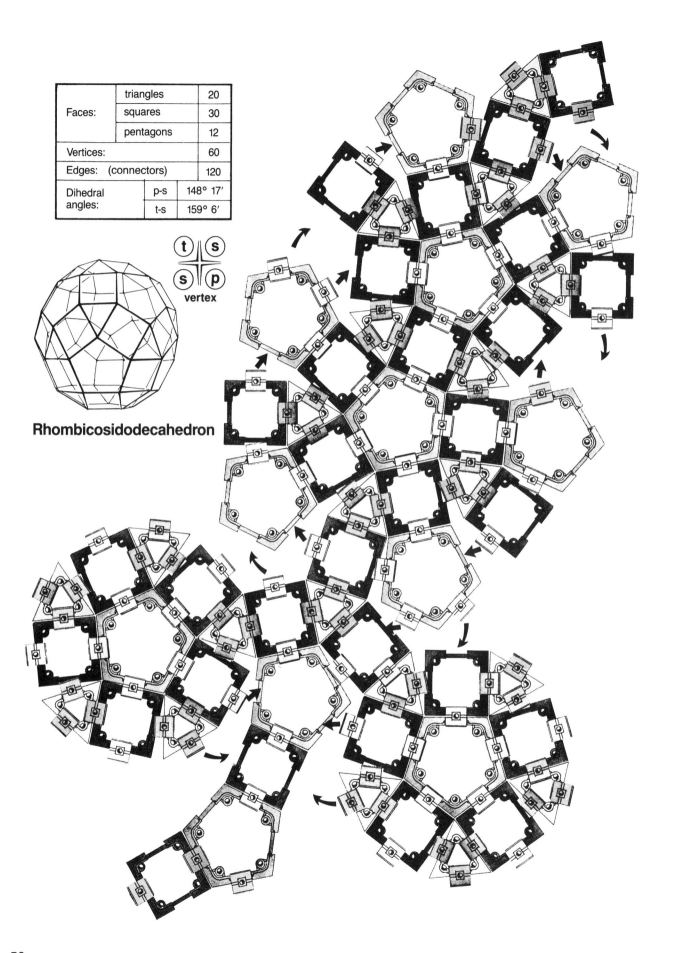

Rhombicosidodecahedron

Bibliography

Beard, Robert S., **Patterns in Space**
Creative Publications, Palo Alto, Calif., 1973

Critchlow, Keith, **Order in Space – a Design Source Book**
Viking Press, New York, 1970, ISBN: 0-500-34033-1

Davidson, Patricia S. and Robert E. Willcutt
Spatial Problem Solving with Cuisenaire Rods
Cuisenaire Company of America, Inc., New Rochelle, N.Y., 1983,
ISBN: 0-914040-99-5

Holden, Alan: **Shapes, Space and Symmetry**
Columbia University Press, New York and London, 1971,
ISBN: 0-231-08323-8

National Council of Teachers of Mathematics
Curriculum and Evaluation Standards for School Mathematics (draft)
National Council of Teachers of Mathematics,
Reston, Virginia, Oct. 87

National Council of Teachers of Mathematics, Ed. Mary Lindquist,
Learning and Teaching Geometry, K - 12, 1987 NCTM Yearbook
National Council of Teachers of Mathematics, Reston, Virginia, 1987
ISBN: 0-87353-235-X

Pearce, Peter, and Susan Pearce, **Polyhedra Primer**
Dale Seymour Publications, Palo Alto California, 1978,
ISBN: 0-442-26496-8

Seymour, Dale, C. Greenes, **Activities with Geoblocks**
Creative Publications, Palo Alto, Calif., 1975,
ISBN: 0-88488-049-4

Winter, Mary Jean, et. al.
Spatial Visualization, The Middle Grades Mathematics Project
Addison Wesley, Menlo Park, Calif. 1986,
ISBN: 0-201-21477-6

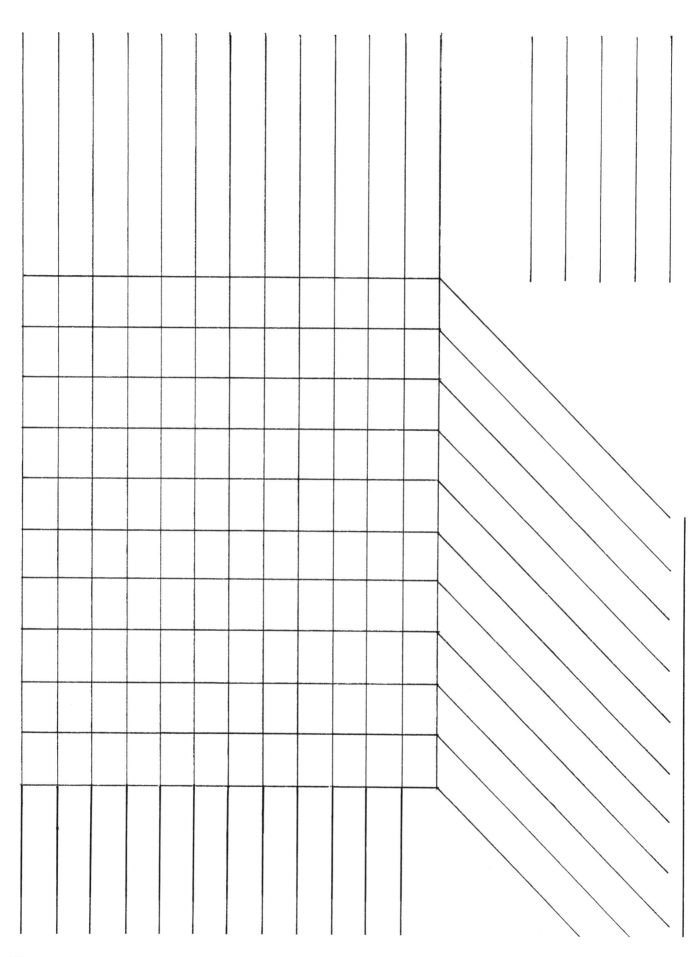